D1529453

Extra Practice
for
PRIMARY
MATHEMATICS

6

TINOH CHAN

PREFACE

Extra Practice *for* Primary Mathematics (U.S. Edition) is a series of six supplementary books that will prove invaluable to students in their understanding of mathematical concepts.

This series follows the topical arrangement in the Primary Mathematics U.S. Edition series. The exercises provide problems of a similar style and level of difficulty as the course material covered in the Primary Mathematics U.S. Edition series. The exercises are short and specific, so instructors may assign only those topics in which the student needs more practice. This, together with the simple language used, will allow students to review mathematics with minimal guidance.

The practice material aims to consolidate and reinforce the mathematical skills taught in the Primary Mathematics series.

© 2004 Marshall Cavendish International (Singapore) Private Limited

Published by Federal – Marshall Cavendish Education
An imprint of Marshall Cavendish International (Singapore) Private Limited
A member of Times Publishing Limited
Times Centre, 1 New Industrial Road, Singapore 536196
Customer Service Hotline: (65) 6213 9106
E-mail: fps@tpl.com.sg

First published 2004

ISBN 981-01-9378-5

Printed in Singapore by Times Graphics Pte Ltd

Distributed by
SingaporeMath.com Inc
404 Beavercreek Road #225
Oregon City, OR 97045
U.S.A.
Website: http://www.singaporemath.com

CONTENTS

Algebra (1)

Do these problems. Show all your work clearly.

(1) Terry spent $x in one shop and $53 in another shop.
    (a) Express the total amount of money spent in terms of x.
    (b) If x = 5, find the total amount of money spent.
    (c) If x = 10, find the total amount of money spent.

a) $x + $53

b) $5 + $63
$x = 5
$5 + 53
= $58.00

c) $10 + $53
$x = 10
$10 + $53
= $63.00

(2) Leela had 24 lb of salt. She packed the salt into bags of Y lb each.
    (a) Express the number of bags she packed in terms of Y.
    (b) If Y = 3, find the number of bags she packed.
    (c) If Y = 4, find the number of bags she packed.

a) 24 ÷ y

b) 24 ÷ 3
y = 3
24 ÷ 3
= 8 bags

c) 24 ÷ 4
y = 4
24 ÷ 4
= 6 bags

(3) Sally had $m. She spent $2.50.
    (a) Express the amount of money she had left in terms of m.
    (b) If m = 10, find the amount of money she had left.
    (c) If m = 5.5, find the amount of money she had left.

a) $m − $2.50
$m

b) $10 − $2.50
$m = 10
$10.00 $2.50
= $6.50

c) $5.50 − 2.50
$m = 5.50
$5.50 − 2.50
= $3.00

(4) A rectangle is L cm long and 5 cm wide.
    (a) Express the area of the rectangle in terms of L.
    (b) If $L = 8$, find the area of the rectangle.
    (c) If $L = 12$, find the area of the rectangle.

(5) Ramli's monthly salary is $\$S$. He spends \$1500 each month.
    (a) Express the amount of money he saves in a year in terms of S.
    (b) If $S = 2300$, find the amount of money he saves in a year.
    (c) If $S = 2800$, find the amount of money he saves in a year.

(6) 5 tins of biscuits, of equal weight, together weigh N grams. Each empty tin weighs 100 grams.
    (a) Express the weight of the biscuits in each tin in terms of N.
    (b) If $N = 6500$, find the weight of the biscuits in each tin.
    (c) If $N = 9000$, find the weight of the biscuits in each tin.

Algebra (2)

A. Find the value of each of the following expressions when $m = 20$.

(1) $m - 13$ =	(2) $8 + m$ =
(3) $5m$ =	(4) $\dfrac{m}{4}$ =
(5) $\dfrac{80}{m}$ =	(6) $29 - m$ =
(7) $3m + 20$ =	(8) $50 - 2m + 15$ =

B. Find the value of each of the following expressions when $h = 10$.

(1) $6h - 15$ =	(2) $\dfrac{h}{2} + 30$ =
(3) $\dfrac{1 + h}{11}$ =	(4) $\dfrac{3h}{h}$ =
(5) $5 + h^2$ =	(6) $2h^2 - 8$ =
(7) $h + \dfrac{h}{10}$ =	(8) $\dfrac{200}{h} - h$ =

C.   Simplify each of the following expressions.

(1) $m + m$ $=$	(2) $N + N + N$ $=$
(3) $4p + 2p$ $=$	(4) $8q + q$ $=$
(5) $7b - 2b$ $=$	(6) $a + 9a + 2a$ $=$
(7) $10g + 3g - 6g$ $=$	(8) $4e - e + 5e$ $=$
(9) $8z + 2z - 5$ $=$	(10) $3t - 6 + 2t$ $=$
(11) $4f - 3f - 6$ $=$	(12) $7d + d + 1$ $=$
(13) $8 + a - 5 + a$ $=$	(14) $3h + 4 - h - 2$ $=$
(15) $6k + 6 + 2k - 6$ $=$	(16) $10 - 3r + 5 + 2r$ $=$

Answer the following questions.

(1) How many faces does each solid have?

(a)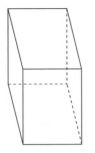

Number of faces: _____

(b)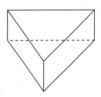

Number of faces: _____

(c)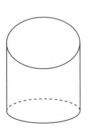

Number of faces: _____

(d)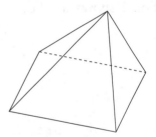

Number of faces: _____

(2) Which of the following can be folded to form a cube? Circle them.

(a)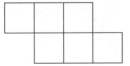

(b)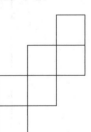

(c)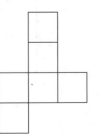

(d)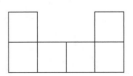

(3) Which of the following can be folded to form a cuboid? Circle them.

(a)

(b)

(c)

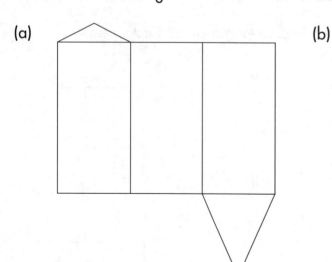

(d)

(4) This figure shows a solid.

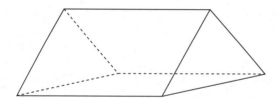

Which of the following can be a net of it? Circle the correct answer.

(a)

(b)

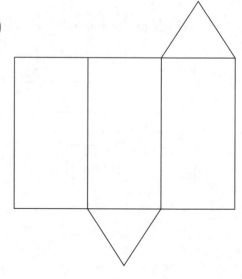

6

(5) This is a net of a solid.

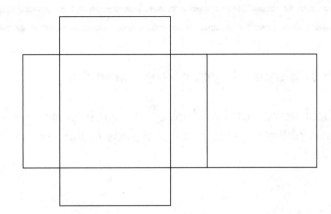

Which one of the following solids can be formed by the above net?
Circle the correct answer.

(a)

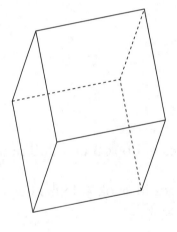

(b)

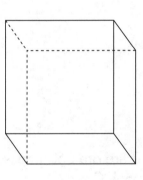

(c)

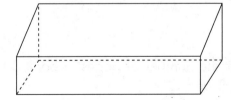

Ratio (1):
Ratio and Fraction

Do these problems. Show all your work clearly.

(1) There are 32 local stamps and 48 foreign stamps in a stamp album.
   (a) Find the ratio of the number of local stamps to the number of foreign stamps.

   (b) Find the ratio of the number of foreign stamps to the number of local stamps.

(2) There are 350 pages in book A, 500 pages in book B and 200 pages in book C.
   (a) What is the ratio of the number of pages in book A to the number of pages in book B to the number of pages in book C?

   (b) What is the ratio of the number of pages in book B to the total number of pages in books A, B and C?

(3) The income of Melissa and Patricia are in the ratio 4 : 5.

Melissa				

| Patricia | | | | | |

(a) What fraction of Patricia's income is Melissa's income?

Melissa's income is [   ] of Patricia's income.

(b) What fraction of the total income of Melissa and Patricia is Patricia's income?

Patricia's income is [   ] of the total income of Melissa and Patricia.

(4) The ratio of the number of bees to the number of butterflies in a picture is 7 : 3.

bees | | | | | | | |

butterflies | | | |

(a) Express the number of bees as a fraction of the number of butterflies.   [   ]

(b) Express the number of butterflies as a fraction of the number of bees.   [   ]

(c) Express the number of bees as a fraction of the total number of bees and butterflies.   [   ]

(5) The ratio of the number of orchids to the number of roses to the number of lilies is 3 : 2 : 6.

orchids ▢▢▢

roses ▢▢

lilies ▢▢▢▢▢▢

(a) What is the ratio of the total number of orchids and roses to the number of lilies?

▢

(b) How many times as many lilies as roses are there?

▢

(c) Express the number of orchids as a fraction of the number of lilies.

▢

(6) Ali's age is $\frac{2}{3}$ of his father's age.

Ali's age ▢▢

Ali's father's age ▢▢▢

(a) What is the ratio of Ali's age to his father's age?

▢

(b) Express Ali's father's age as a fraction of Ali's age.

▢

(7) The ratio of the number of volleyballs to the number of basketballs in the P.E. room is 4 : 7. There are 21 basketballs. How many volleyballs are there?

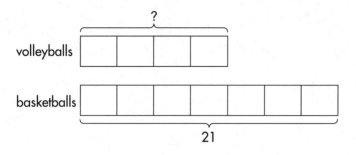

(8) The length, width and height of a box are in the ratio 2 : 5 : 3. The length of the box is 6 cm. Find the sum of the width and the height of the box.

6 cm

length

width

height

?

(9) The total of 3 numbers, A, B and C is 90. The ratio of A to B is 3 : 2. The ratio of B to C is 2 : 5. What are the 3 numbers?

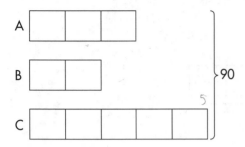

(10) The ratio of the number of times Marie skips to the number of times Jed skips is 2 : 3. The ratio of the number of times Jed skips to the number of times Petra skips is 6 : 5.

Marie [50 | 50] 100

Jed

Petra   ?

(a) Find the ratio of the number of times Marie skips to the number of times Petra skips.

(b) If Marie skips 100 times, how many times does Petra skip?

(11) The ratio of the number of apples in identical baskets A, B and C is 12 : 8 : 9. Basket A and basket B weigh 10 kg altogether. Find the total weight of the 3 baskets of apples.

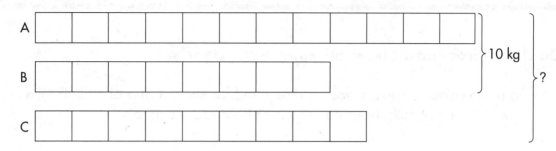

(12) A rectangular plot of land measures 90 m by 50 m. A farmer plants cucumbers and tomatoes on it, with the land areas used for the crops being 2 : 3 respectively. How much more land do the tomatoes take up than the cucumbers?

cucumbers

tomatoes

Ratio (2): Ratio and Proportion

Do these problems. Show all your work clearly.

(1)   To make cakes, 3 cups of flour are required for every 1 cup of milk. If Miss Peng uses 10 cups of milk, how many cups of flour are required?

(2)   The ratio of sugar to water in a sugar solution is 1 : 19 by weight. Find the amount of sugar in 1 kg of the solution.

(3) The sides of a triangle are in the ratio 4 : 3 : 2. If the perimeter is 29 cm, find the lengths of its sides.

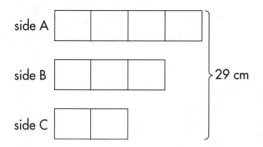

(4) The ratio of the length of a rectangular piece of paper to its width is 5 : 3. Find the perimeter of the piece of paper if its length is 50 cm.

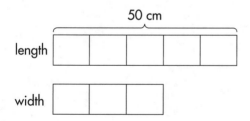

(5)　In my stamp album, there are 8 U.S. stamps to every 5 Canadian stamps.
If there are 32 U.S. stamps, find the total number of stamps in my stamp album.

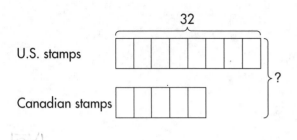

54

(6)　The ratio of Paul's test points to Peter's test points is 3 : 2. If Peter's score is lower
than Paul's by 28 points, what is their total score?

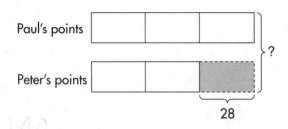

140

Ratio (3):
Changing Ratios

Do these problems. Show all your work clearly.

(1) The ratio of the number of Susan's books to Luigi's is 3 : 4. Luigi has 60 books. If Luigi gives 30 books to Susan, what will the new ratio of the number of Susan's books to Luigi's be?

(2) Andrew and Dan had an equal amount of money each. After Andrew earned $15 more and Dan earned $10 more, the ratio of Andrew's money to Dan's money became 8 : 7. How much money did each boy have at first?

(3) At a track meet, $\frac{1}{5}$ of the people participated in the high jump. However, 2 more participants joined later, causing the ratio of the number of participants in the high jump to those not participating to be 1 : 3. How many people were at the meet?

(4) The ratio of the number of mints in Jar A to that in Jar B was 8 : 5. After $\frac{1}{4}$ of the mints in Jar A were sold, there were 120 more mints in Jar A than Jar B. How many mints were there in Jar B?

(5) Some workers are digging a drain. The ratio of the length that has already been

dug to that which has not been dug is 3 : 4. After another 20 m of the drain has been dug, this ratio becomes 4 : 3. What is the total length of the drain to be dug?

(6) The ratio of the number of people in Team A to that in Team B is 7 : 3. If 30 people from Team A join Team B, the ratio of the number of people in Team A to that in Team B will become 3 : 2. How many people are there in each team?

Percentage (1):
Part of a Whole as a Percentage

A. Express each of the following as a percentage.

(1)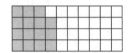

$\dfrac{15}{40} =$

(2)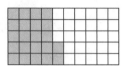

$\dfrac{22}{50} =$

(3)

$\dfrac{38}{100} =$

(4)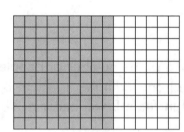

$\dfrac{90}{150} =$

B. Write each fraction as a percentage.

(1)  $\dfrac{1}{4} =$

(2)  $\dfrac{2}{5} =$

(3)  $\dfrac{5}{8} =$

C. Write each fraction as a percentage.

(1) $\dfrac{32}{100}$ =	(2) $\dfrac{1}{10}$ =
(3) $\dfrac{6}{30}$ =	(4) $\dfrac{3}{8}$ =
(5) $\dfrac{28}{35}$ =	(6) $\dfrac{11}{88}$ =
(7) $\dfrac{50}{125}$ =	(8) $\dfrac{240}{400}$ =

D. Express each percentage as a fraction in its simplest form.

(1) 4% =	(2) 8% =
(3) 17% =	(4) 30% =
(5) 73% =	(6) 80% =
(7) 99% =	(8) 100% =

E. **Express each decimal as a percentage.**

(1) 0.5 =	(2) 0.01 =
(3) 0.26 =	(4) 0.48 =
(5) 0.012 =	(6) 0.007 =
(7) 0.403 =	(8) 0.391 =

F. **Express each percentage as a decimal.**

(1) 3% =	(2) 6% =
(3) 7% =	(4) 29% =
(5) 33% =	(6) 56% =
(7) 70% =	(8) 90% =

Percentage (2): Writing Fractions as Percentages

Write each of the following as a percentage.

(1) 6 out of 30	(2) 36 out of 90
(3) 35 out of 70	(4) 60 out of 80
(5) 30 out of 50	(6) 15 out of 60
(7) 36 out of 200	(8) 40 out of 500
(9) 48 out of 300	(10) 98 out of 200
(11) 80 out of 400	(12) 75 out of 500

Do these problems. Show all your work clearly.

(1)   Express $4 as a percentage of $50.

(2)   Express 780 m as a percentage of 1.5 km.

(3)   Express 45 min as a percentage of $2\frac{1}{2}$ h.

(4)   Express 960 g as a percentage of 3 kg.

(5)   Express 700 ml as a percentage of 2.8 ℓ.

(6) Express 80¢ as a percentage of 50¢.

(7) Express 1 m as a percentage of 500 cm.

(8) Express 1 ft as a percentage of 10 in.

(9) Express 2 years 3 months as a percentage of 10 months.

(10) Express 2.4 qt as a percentage of 1.5 gal.

Percentage (4): Word Problems

Do these problems. Show all your work clearly.

(1)   Suni had $52. She spent 30% of it. How much money did she spend?

(2)   The cost price of a computer was $760. It was sold at a discount of 15%. What was the selling price?

(3)   There were 30 workers in a factory in May. In June, the number of workers increased by 20%. How many workers were there in June?

(4)   A supermarket stocked 210 kg of sugar. 55% was sold in a week. How many kilograms of sugar were left unsold at the end of that week?

(5) In 1995, the school stamp club had 660 members. In 1996, it had 600 members. What was the percentage decrease in membership?

(6) Margie deposits $2500 in a bank. The bank pays 6.5% interest per year. What is the total amount of money that she can withdraw after 1 year?

(7) If 35% of a number is $612\frac{1}{2}$, what is the number?

(8) I gave 10% of my money to Joanne, 20% to Kathy and kept the remaining $140 for myself. How much money did Kathy get?

(9) Susan and her family ate 65% of a bowl of cherries. They had 105 cherries left. How many cherries did they have at first?

(10) Adam's income was increased by 5% in May. If he received $1102.50 in May, find his income in April.

(11) Tom's age is 80% less than that of his grandfather. If Tom is 12 years old, how old is his grandfather?

(12) Lynn had 50 balloons. 40% of them burst and 20% of the remainder were given to Cameron. How many balloons did Lynn have left?

Do these problems. Show all your work clearly.

(1) A computer was priced at $1080. As business was bad, the shopkeeper decided to sell it at 80% of the original price. How much less was the computer sold for?

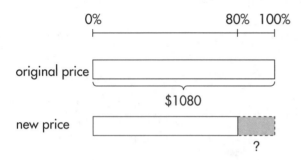

(2) The number of students in a school was increased by 5% at the end of the year to 1260. What was the number of students at the beginning of the year?

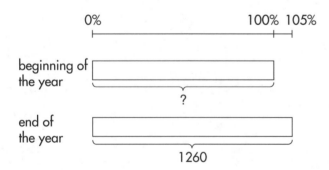

(3) Suni spent $27. This was 30% of her savings. Calculate her savings.

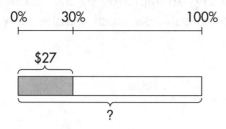

(4) Rose donated 25% of her story books to charity. After the donation, she still had 1500 story books on her bookshelf. Calculate the number of story books she had at first.

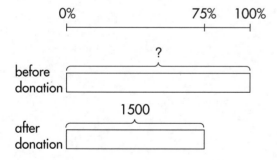

(5) In her first test, Jasmine scored 80 points for English and 90 points for Mathematics. In her second test, her score for English improved by 5%, but her score for Mathematics fell by 10%. In her second test, how much did she score for English and Mathematics separately?

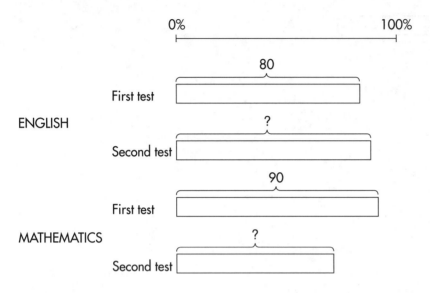

(6) Sam weighed 85 kg in May and 4% less in June. Calculate his weight in June.

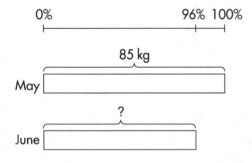

(7)   20% of a pile of rice in the warehouse was transported away yesterday and 2720 kg was transported away today. The remaining amount of rice is 48% of the original. How many kilograms of rice did the warehouse have at first?

(8)   A businessman earned $5000 in June this year. If his pay went up by 20% every month, how much money would he earn altogether in June, July and August?

Speed (1)

A. Complete the following table.

	Distance	Time	Speed
(1)	360 mi	5 h	
(2)		3 h	65 mi/h
(3)	480 mi		80 mi/h

B. Do these problems. Show all your work clearly.

(1) The average speed of a cyclist is $20\frac{1}{2}$ km/h. How far does he travel in 4 hours?

(2) An airplane completed a 4250 km journey in 5 hours. What was its average speed?

(3) How many kilometers can Jeremy walk in $3\frac{1}{4}$ h if his average speed of walking is 50 m/min?

(4) Josh bicycled from town X to town Y which was 75 km away. He left town X at 8:45 a.m. and bicycled at 15 km/h. At what time did he reach town Y?

(5) Jane traveled to town A by bus. The bus traveled at 50 mi/h for 3 hours. She then walked to her grandfather's house at 2 mi/h for an hour and a half. What was the total distance traveled by Jane?

(6) A motorist drove 108 km in 1 h 30 min. How far did he travel in 50 min if he drove at the same rate throughout his journey?

(7) Car A traveled 216 km in 3 hours and car B traveled 260 km in 4 hours.
    (a) Which car traveled faster?
    (b) How much faster was it?

(8) Mark drove at a certain speed of 65 km/h for 3 hours and 73 km/h for 2 hours. What was his average speed for the whole journey?

(9) It is 480 km from town A to town B. Hassan took 6 hours to complete the journey. At this same average speed, how long would he take to reach town C, which is 240 km away?

(10) Danny drove a distance of 260 mi at 65 mi/h. Then he stopped for 30 minutes to have his lunch. After lunch, he covered the rest of his journey at 55 mi/h. If the second part of his journey was 165 mi, how long did he take for the whole journey?

Speed (2)

Do these problems. Show all your work clearly.

(1) Zachary traveled from city A to city B. He left city A at 7:30 a.m. and reached city B at 12 noon. Find his average speed if city B is 180 mi away from city A.

(2) Janet drives at a uniform speed of 68 km/h. Sharon drives at a uniform speed of 50 km/h. What is the difference in the distances they travel in $2\frac{1}{2}$ hours?

(3) Fanny drove at an average speed of 80 km/h for $\frac{3}{4}$ hour and then at 55 km/h for $1\frac{1}{5}$ hours. What was the total distance of her journey?

(4) Lisa ran around a rectangular field 150 m long and 50 m wide at an average speed of 100 m/min. How long did she take to complete 5 rounds?

(5)   Amy drove 130 mi from town X to town Y at a uniform speed of 60 mi/h. She left town X at 11:20 a.m. At what time did she reach town Y?

(6)   In a race, Justin bicycled at an average speed of 15 km/h for the first 10 km and at an average speed of 12 km/h for the remaining 6 km. Find his average speed for the whole journey in kilometers per hour.

Do these problems. Show all your work clearly.

(1) The distance between A and B is 3400 m. Lisa walks from A to B in 40 minutes and takes 5 minutes more to return to A. What is Lisa's average speed in m/min for the whole journey from A to B and back to A again?

(2) An airplane flew from A to B in 3 hours, covering a distance of 540 km per hour. On the return trip, as the weather was bad, the average speed was reduced by 60 km/h. How many hours did the airplane take to return from B to A?

(3) A sports car travels from A at a speed of 84 km/h, and reaches B in $1\frac{1}{2}$ hours. A normal car travels at $\frac{2}{3}$ of the sports car's speed. How many hours does the normal car take to reach B?

(4) A train is 143 m long. It moves towards a tunnel at a speed of 15 m/s. It takes 3 min 42 s for the entire length of the train to pass through the tunnel. How long is this tunnel?

(5) A car travels from X to Y in 3 hours at a speed of 35 km/h. If the speed is increased by 20%, how much earlier will the car reach Y, in minutes?

(6) Cities W and Z are 280 km apart. A train traveled for $3\frac{1}{2}$ hours, and covered 75% of the whole journey. Find the average speed of the train.

A. Choose the correct answer and write its number in the parentheses provided.

(1) Express $\frac{3}{8}$ as a decimal.
    (1) 37.5   (2) 3.75   (3) 0.375   (4) 0.0375 ( )

(2) Express 15% as a fraction in its simplest form.
    (1) $\frac{1}{15}$ (2) $\frac{5}{16}$ (3) $\frac{3}{20}$ (4) $\frac{4}{25}$ ( )

(3) 0.75% = _____
    (1) 750   (2) 7.5   (3) 0.075   (4) 0.0075 ( )

(4) Write $\frac{4}{5}$ as a percentage.
    (1) 20%   (2) 40%   (3) 60%   (4) 80%   ( )

(5) Which of the following is correct?
    (1) 0.16 = 160%   (2) 3.2 = 320%
    (3) 0.027 = 270%   (4) 41 = 410%   ( )

(6) Write 0.046 as a percentage.
    (1) 0.46%   (2) 4.6%   (3) 46%   (4) 460% ( )

(7) What percentage of $4.80 is $2.16?
    (1) 35%   (2) 45%   (3) 55%   (4) 65% ( )

(8) Express 45 min as a percentage of 2 h.
    (1) 37.5%   (2) 38.4%   (3) 39.3%   (4) 39.5% ( )

(9)

The hour hand of an alarm clock is 4 cm long. How far does the tip of the hour hand travel when it moves in the clockwise direction from the digit 12 to the digit 3? (Take π = 3.14.)

    (1) 8.38 cm   (2) 7.48 cm
    (3) 6.28 cm   (4) 5.18 cm   ( )

(10) The number of students in our school increased by 6% this year. If there are 1643 students in our school this year, how many students were there last year?
   (1) 1550 students   (2) 1556 students
   (3) 1567 students   (4) 1576 students   (   )

B. Fill in the blanks.

(1) When $n = 7$, the value of $n - \dfrac{n}{14}$ is _____.

$$\boxed{}$$

(2) Mrs. Cai bought x grams of ground coffee. She used y grams a day. How many grams of ground coffee would be left after 10 days?

grams

(3) The ratio of the volume of two cubes A and B is 9 : 7. The volume of cube A is ⬚ of the volume of cube B.

(4) Mimi read 20 books during the school holidays. 6 of them were in Spanish. The rest were in English. The ratio of the number of English books to the total number of books Mimi read was ⬚.

(5) I shared 132 used stamps with Kumar and Jamilah in the ratio of 3 : 5 : 4. How many used stamps did Kumar get?

stamps

(6) A shopkeeper sold 36 kg of rice on Monday and 25 kg 650 g of rice on Tuesday. The percentage decrease in the amount of rice sold is ⬚.

%

(7) Darla bought 5 lb of beef. She ate 30% of it. How many pounds of beef were left over?

lbs

(8) Julie took 1 hour to walk 7 km. At this speed, how long did she take to walk from her house to the post office which was 1.75 km away?

min

(9) Gary deposited a sum of money in a bank. The bank paid 7% interest per year. He received $175 interest at the end of the year. How much was the deposit?

$

C. Do these problems. Show all your work clearly.

(1) Danny drove at an average speed of 60 km/h for 30 min and 70 km/h for $1\frac{1}{2}$ hours. What was his average speed for the whole journey?

(2) Raoul and Lisa's savings are in the ratio of 3 : 1. If Raoul gives Lisa $240, the new ratio will be 3 : 5. How much money does each of them have?

Fractions: Division (1)

A. Divide. Write all answers in their simplest form. Change answers to whole or mixed numbers where possible.

(1) $6 \div \frac{2}{3} =$	(2) $6 \div \frac{3}{5} =$
(3) $7 \div \frac{1}{4} =$	(4) $5 \div \frac{1}{4} =$
(5) $15 \div \frac{2}{3} =$	(6) $9 \div \frac{3}{4} =$
(7) $3 \div \frac{7}{10} =$	(8) $18 \div \frac{6}{5} =$
(9) $\frac{4}{5} \div 3 =$	(10) $\frac{2}{3} \div 6 =$
(11) $\frac{3}{8} \div 3 =$	(12) $\frac{11}{5} \div 3 =$
(13) $\frac{5}{12} \div 10 =$	(14) $\frac{3}{8} \div 2 =$

B. Divide. Write all answers in their simplest form. Change answers to whole or mixed numbers where possible.

(1) $\dfrac{7}{8} \div \dfrac{3}{2} =$	(2) $\dfrac{7}{8} \div \dfrac{15}{16} =$
(3) $\dfrac{4}{3} \div \dfrac{3}{10} =$	(4) $\dfrac{1}{4} \div \dfrac{3}{4} =$
(5) $\dfrac{3}{8} \div \dfrac{5}{8} =$	(6) $\dfrac{5}{6} \div \dfrac{25}{24} =$
(7) $\dfrac{9}{10} \div \dfrac{3}{5} =$	(8) $\dfrac{1}{6} \div \dfrac{1}{3} =$
(9) $\dfrac{3}{4} \div \dfrac{5}{8} =$	(10) $\dfrac{3}{4} \div \dfrac{5}{3} =$
(11) $\dfrac{4}{5} \div \dfrac{9}{4} =$	(12) $\dfrac{7}{9} \div \dfrac{7}{36} =$
(13) $\dfrac{15}{32} \div \dfrac{5}{64} =$	(14) $\dfrac{36}{35} \div \dfrac{15}{14} =$
(15) $\dfrac{7}{8} \div \dfrac{1}{3} =$	(16) $\dfrac{7}{9} \div \dfrac{1}{7} =$

Do these problems. Show all your work clearly.

(1)   How many $\frac{1}{8}$'s are there in 2.5?

(2)   How many $\frac{1}{4}$-quart glasses may be filled from 12 quarts of lemonade?

(3)   How many times must a $\frac{2}{3}$-quart spray bottle be filled in order to use up 8 qt of window cleaner?

(4)   Each guest at a party will eat $\frac{5}{16}$ lb of cashews. How many guests will be served with 10 lb of cashews?

Fractions:
Order of Operation

A. Find the value of the following. Write all answers in their simplest form. Change answers to whole or mixed numbers where possible.

(1) $\frac{3}{5} + \frac{1}{6} - \frac{1}{2} =$	(2) $\frac{7}{3} + \frac{2}{5} + 1\frac{1}{10} =$
(3) $\frac{1}{2} - \frac{1}{4} - \frac{1}{8} =$	(4) $\frac{3}{4} - \frac{1}{2} + \frac{2}{3} =$
(5) $\frac{5}{8} - \frac{1}{2} + \frac{1}{4} =$	(6) $\frac{5}{6} + \frac{5}{8} - \frac{1}{3} =$
(7) $3\frac{1}{2} - 1\frac{1}{6} + 2\frac{2}{3} =$	(8) $\frac{1}{2} \times \frac{1}{3} \div \frac{1}{4} =$
(9) $\frac{1}{2} \times \frac{5}{12} \div \frac{5}{6} =$	(10) $\frac{1}{2} \div \frac{5}{12} \times \frac{5}{6} =$
(11) $\frac{1}{2} \div \frac{1}{3} \times \frac{1}{4} =$	(12) $\frac{1}{2} \div \frac{1}{3} \times 4 =$
(13) $\frac{1}{2} \div \frac{5}{12} \div \frac{5}{6} =$	(14) $14 \times \frac{2}{7} \div 2 =$

B. **Find the value of the following. Write all answers in their simplest form. Change answers to whole or mixed numbers where possible.**

(1) $\frac{1}{3} + \frac{1}{2} \times \frac{4}{5} =$

(2) $\frac{2}{5} - \frac{4}{9} \times \frac{3}{4} =$

(3) $\frac{4}{3} \times \frac{3}{8} + \frac{3}{4} \times \frac{1}{4} =$

(4) $3 \times \frac{1}{4} \div \frac{5}{2} + \frac{1}{3} \times \frac{3}{5} =$

(5) $\frac{1}{2} + 3 \times \frac{3}{2} \div 2 - \frac{3}{8} =$

(6) $6 \times \frac{1}{3} \times \frac{2}{9} - \frac{4}{5} \times \frac{1}{2} =$

(7) $12 \div 2 \times \frac{1}{4} \div \frac{3}{2} - \frac{1}{2} \times \frac{2}{3} =$

(8) $4 + \frac{2}{3} \times \frac{1}{6} \div \frac{1}{2} - 1 =$

C. Find the value of the following. Write all answers in their simplest form. Change answers to whole or mixed numbers where possible.

(1) $\left(\frac{1}{3} + \frac{1}{6} \right) \times \frac{1}{2} =$

(2) $\frac{4}{3} \times \left(\frac{3}{5} - \frac{3}{20} \right) =$

(3) $4 \times \left(\frac{1}{3} + \frac{1}{6} \right) \div 8 =$

(4) $\left(\frac{8}{5} - \frac{7}{10} \right) \div \frac{3}{5} =$

(5) $6 \div \left(\frac{3}{5} - \frac{3}{10} \right) \times \frac{1}{5} =$

(6) $32 \times \frac{3}{8} \times \left(\frac{1}{2} - \frac{1}{4} \right) \div 3 =$

(7) $\left(\frac{5}{6} - \frac{7}{12} \right) - \frac{1}{3} \times \frac{3}{4} \div 3 =$

(8) $2 \times \frac{2}{3} \times \left(\frac{1}{2} - \frac{1}{8} \right) \div 3 - \frac{2}{3} \div 8 =$

Do these problems. Show all your work clearly.

(1) May has 84 books. $\frac{3}{4}$ of them are fiction books. $\frac{2}{3}$ of the fiction books are on science fiction. How many science fiction books are there?

(2) Mrs. Ray sold 96 lb of shrimp. $\frac{3}{4}$ of it was sold at $5.60 per pound and the rest at $4.70 per pound. How much money did she receive altogether?

(3)   Eric had 28 kg of soy beans. He gave $3\frac{1}{5}$ kg to his wife and packed the rest equally into bags. If each bag contained $\frac{4}{5}$ kg of soy beans, how many bags could he pack?

(4)   There were five bags of wheat. Three of them contained $2\frac{5}{9}$ lb of wheat each. Two of them contained $4\frac{1}{6}$ lb of wheat each. What was the average weight of the five bags of wheat?

(5) Andy has $7\frac{3}{4}$ qt of fruit juice more than Molly. Molly has $3\frac{1}{2}$ qt of fruit juice less than Sami. Sami has $13\frac{2}{3}$ qt of fruit juice. How much fruit juice do Andy and Molly have altogether?

(6) Jim gave $\frac{3}{8}$ of his stickers to Hashim and $\frac{1}{4}$ of them to Rani. He had 21 stickers left. How many stickers did he have at first?

(7) Muthu reads 20 pages of a book in a day. After 6 days, $\frac{2}{5}$ of the book is still unread. How many pages are there in this book?

(8) After $\frac{1}{6}$ of a barrel of rice was eaten, 10 kg of the rice was left. How many kg of rice would be left after $\frac{1}{4}$ of it had been eaten?

(9) After spending $\frac{3}{5}$ of his money, Larry received a cash gift of $250 from his uncle. At this time, the amount of money which he had was $\frac{1}{2}$ of the amount which he had at first. How much money did he have at first?

(10) A school had 400 girls last year, and the number of boys was 95 more than that of the girls. This year, the number of girls has increased by $\frac{1}{5}$ of last year's number and is 30 more than the number of boys. By what fraction has the number of boys been reduced?

Circles (1)

A. Find the circumference of each circle.

(1)

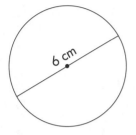

(Take π = 3.14)

(2)

(Take π = 3.14)

(3)

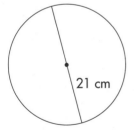

(Take π = $\frac{22}{7}$)

(4)

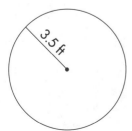

(Take π = $\frac{22}{7}$)

B. Find the area of each circle.

(1)

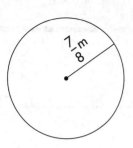

(Take $\pi = \frac{22}{7}$)

(2)

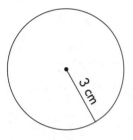

(Take $\pi = 3.14$)

(3)

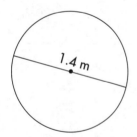

(Take $\pi = \frac{22}{7}$)

(4)

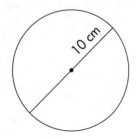

(Take $\pi = 3.14$)

Do these problems. Show all your work clearly.

(1) The figure below is made up of a semicircle and a rectangle. Find the perimeter of the figure. (Take $\pi = \frac{22}{7}$.)

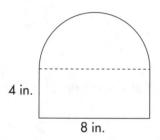

4 in.

8 in.

(2) The figure below is made up of three semicircles and a rectangle. Find the total area of the **unshaded** parts. (Take $\pi = 3.14$.)

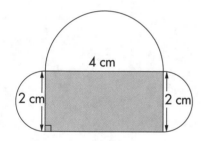

4 cm

2 cm   2 cm

(3) The figure below shows a quarter circle within a right-angled triangle. Find the total area of the shaded parts. (Take $\pi = \frac{22}{7}$.)

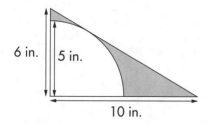

6 in.   5 in.

10 in.

(4) The figure below shows a semicircle within a rectangle. Find the area of the shaded part. Give your answer correct to 1 decimal place. (Take π = 3.14.)

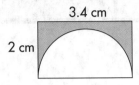

3.4 cm

2 cm

(5) The figure below shows 4 circles within a square. Find the total area of the shaded parts. (Take π = 3.14.)

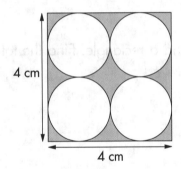

4 cm

4 cm

(6) In the figure below, the shaded parts are semicircles. Find the perimeter of this figure. (Take π = 3.14.)

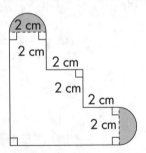

2 cm
2 cm
2 cm
2 cm
2 cm
2 cm

(7) The figure below shows three semicircles within a square. Find the area of the shaded part. (Take π = 3.14.)

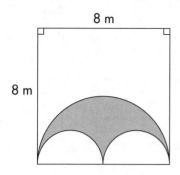

8 m

8 m

(8) The figure below shows a right-angled triangle, a quarter circle and 2 half-quarter circles. Find the area of the shaded part. (Take $\pi = \frac{22}{7}$.)

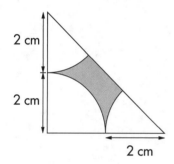

2 cm

2 cm

2 cm

(9) The following figure is made up of 2 rectangles and 2 quarter circles. Find its area. (Take π = 3.14.)

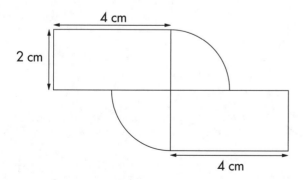

4 cm

2 cm

4 cm

(10) The figure below shows four semicircles cut out from a square. Find the perimeter of the figure. (Take π = 3.14.)

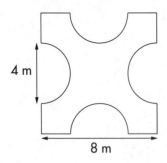

4 m

8 m

(11) The figure below shows a quarter circle and a semicircle within a square. Find the perimeter of the unshaded part. (Take $\pi = \frac{22}{7}$.)

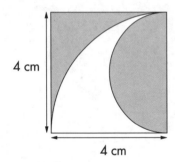

4 cm

4 cm

(12) The figure below shows a rectangle and a circle. The circumference of the circle is 31.4 cm. The area of the rectangle is the same as that of the circle. Find the area of the shaded part. (Take π = 3.14.)

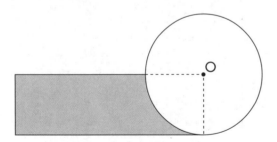

O

Graphs (1)

A. **The pie chart below shows how Lena spent her time yesterday.**

(1) What fraction of Lena's time was spent studying?

(2) What percentage of her time was spent on other activities ('others')?

%

(3) How many hours did she spend playing?

hr

(4) What is the ratio of the time spent sleeping to the time spent playing?

(5) What percentage of her time was **not** spent studying?

%

B. **The pie chart below shows the number of toys in a toy box.**

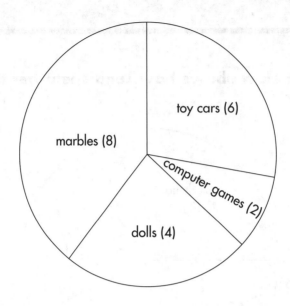

(1) How many toys are there altogether in the toy box?

(2) What percentage of the toys are computer games?

%

(3) What fraction of the toys are marbles?

(4) Express the number of dolls as a percentage of the number of toy cars.

(5) What is the ratio of the number of marbles to the number of computer games to the number of dolls?

A. The pie chart below shows the favorite types of books of a group of 40 students.

(1) What fraction of the students like science fiction?

(2) How many students like animal stories?

(3) What types of books did most students like?

(4) What percentage of the students like jokes? %

(5) What is the ratio of the students who like jokes to the total number of students?

B. **The pie chart below shows how a group of 100 students go to school every day.**

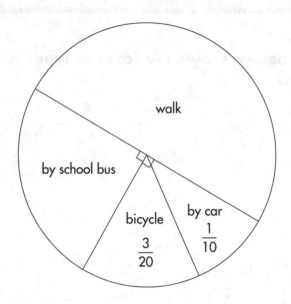

(1) What fraction of the students walk to school?

(2) What percentage of the students go to school by school bus?   %

(3) How many students go to school by car?

(4) How many more students go to school by taking the school bus than by bicycling?

(5) Find the ratio of the students who walk to school to those who go by car.

A. The pie chart below shows how Britney spent her money at the market last Sunday. She spent $50 in all.

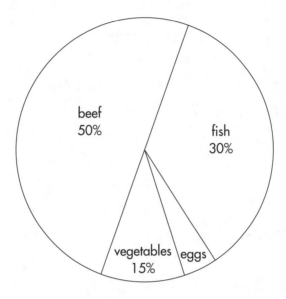

(1) What percentage of Britney's money was spent on eggs?

%

(2) How much did Britney spend on fish?

(3) What fraction of Britney's money was spent on beef?

(4) How much more did Britney spend on vegetables than on eggs?

(5) What is the ratio of the amount spent on fish to the amount spent on beef?

B. **The pie chart below shows the percentages of 800 students who played different sports.**

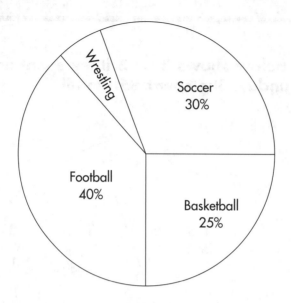

(1) How many did wrestling?

(2) What fraction of the students did soccer?

(3) Altogether, how many students did football or basketball?

(4) There are _____ fewer students who did basketball than soccer.

(5) The ratio of the number of students who did football to the number of students who did soccer to the number of students who did basketball is _____.

Volume (1)

A. Each of the following solids is made up of 2-cm cubes. Find the volume of each solid.

(1)

(2)

(3)

(4)

B. **How many cubes of edge 3 cm are needed to build each of the following cuboids?**

(1)

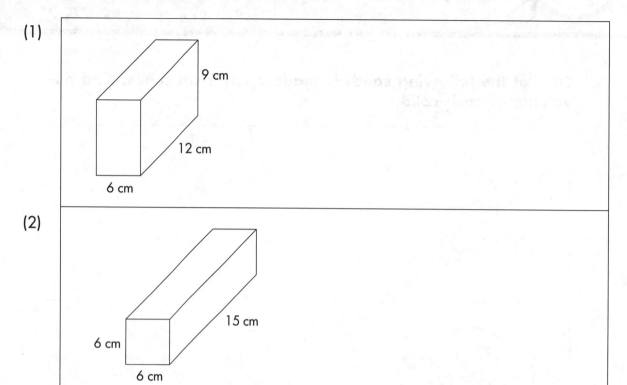

9 cm

12 cm

6 cm

(2)

15 cm

6 cm

6 cm

C. **Find the height of each cuboid.**

(1)

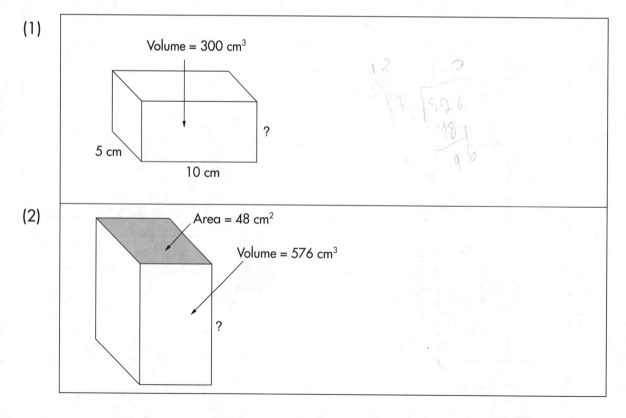

Volume = 300 cm³

?

5 cm

10 cm

(2)

Area = 48 cm²

Volume = 576 cm³

?

Do these problems. Show all your work clearly.

(1) The volume of a cuboid is 189 in.^{3}. What is its length if its height is 7 in. and its width is 3 in.?

(2) Calculate the base area of a cuboid of volume 175 cm^3 and height 7 cm.

(3) A rectangular tank is 25 cm long, 16 cm wide and 30 cm high. It contains 8 ℓ of water. How many more liters of water can it contain? (1 ℓ = 1000 cm^3)

(4) The volume of a wooden block is 1200 cm³. Its length is 5 cm more than its width. If its length is 10 cm, find its height.

(5) A rectangular tank 30 cm by 20 cm by 40 cm is $\frac{2}{5}$ filled with water. How many liters of water must be added to make the tank full? (1 ℓ = 1000 cm³)

(6) A tank 30 cm long, 10 cm wide and 50 cm high is full of water. If the water is poured into containers measuring 5 cm long, 2 cm wide and 10 cm high, how many such containers are needed?

Do these problems. Show all your work clearly.

(1)   A rectangular tank 20 cm long, 30 cm wide and 40 cm high was completely filled with water. If Susan took out 7.5 ℓ of water from the tank, by how many cm did the water level drop? (1 ℓ = 1000 cm³)

(2)   A rectangular tank 30 cm long, 20 cm wide and 50 cm high contains 7 ℓ of water. How many liters of water are needed to raise the water level to $\frac{2}{5}$ of the height of the tank?

(3)   A rectangular fish tank 60 cm long, 35 cm wide and 50 cm high is 80% filled with water. How many jugs full of water can be scooped out from the tank if each jug holds 2 ℓ of water? (1 ℓ = 1000 cm^3)

(4)   A rectangular container of volume 3600 cm^3 is $\frac{3}{4}$ full of water. If all the water from the container is poured to fill a tank 15 cm long and 20 cm high, what is the width of the tank?

Do these problems. Show all your work clearly.

(1) A rectangular tank 17 cm long and 10 cm wide holds 2040 cm³ of water. A small iron cube of side 3 cm is thrown into the tank. What is the new height of the water in the tank? (Give your answer correct to 1 decimal place.)

(2) A rectangular tank 40 cm long and 30 cm wide contains water to a height of 24 cm. When some metal cubes of edge 10 cm are placed in the water, the water level rises to 29 cm. How many metal cubes are there in the tank?

(3)   A rectangular tank 50 cm long and 60 cm wide contains some water and one metal cube of edge 10 cm. The height of the water is 30 cm. By how many centimeters will the water level rise if David puts in 6 more similar metal cubes?

(4)   A rectangular tank 30 cm long, 20 cm wide and 50 cm high contains only some metal balls. The volume of the metal balls is 5000 cm^3 each. The tank is being filled with water flowing from a tap at a rate of 2 liters per minute. If it takes 5 minutes to fill up the tank, how many metal balls are there in the tank?
(1 ℓ = 1000 cm^3)

A. The following figures are not drawn to scale. Find the unknown marked angle in each figure.

(1)

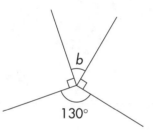

(2)

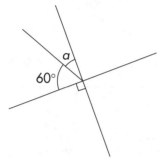

(3)

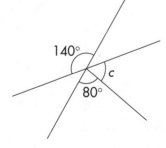

(4)

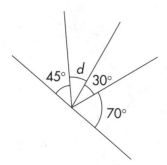

B. The following figures are not drawn to scale. Find the unknown marked angle in each figure.

(1)	(2)
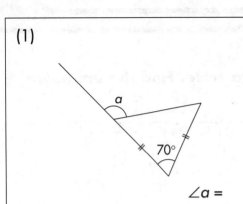 ∠a =	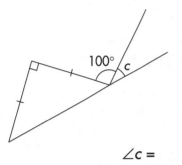 ∠b =

(3)	(4)
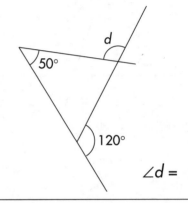 ∠c =	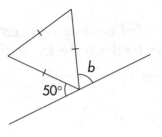 ∠d =

(5)	(6)
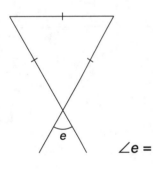 ∠e =	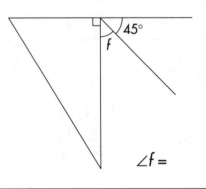 ∠f =

(7)	(8)
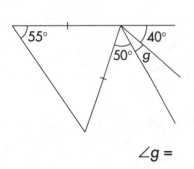 ∠g =	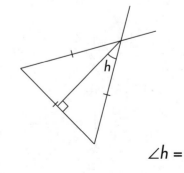 ∠h =

C. The following figures are not drawn to scale.

(1) ABCD is a parallelogram. Find ∠i.

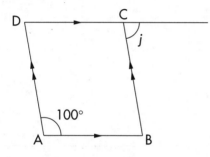

(2) ABCD is a parallelogram. Find ∠j.

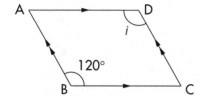

(3) ABCD is a parallelogram. Find ∠k.

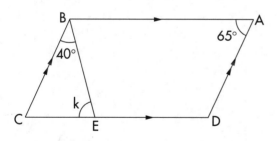

(4) ABCD is a square. Find ∠ℓ.

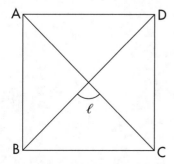

(5) ABCD is a parallelogram. Find ∠m.

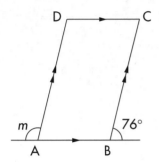

(6) ABCD is a rhombus. CBE is a straight line. Find ∠n.

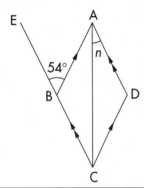

(7) ABCD is a parallelogram. Find ∠p.

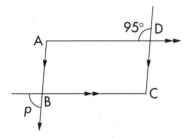

(8) ABC is a triangle. DE//CB. Find ∠q.

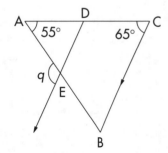

The following figures are not drawn to scale.

(1) ABCD is a square. △AEB is an isosceles triangle. AC is a straight line. Find ∠a.

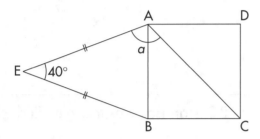

(2) ABCD is a parallelogram. DCE // FH. Find ∠b.

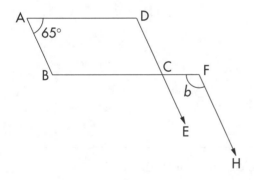

(3) ABCD is a parallelogram. CEF is a triangle. Find ∠c.

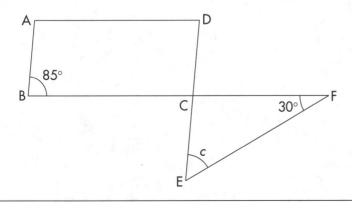

(4) ABCD is a parallelogram. Find ∠d.

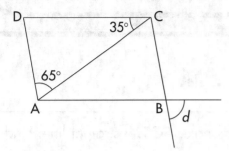

(5) ABCD is a parallelogram. AC // FD. △ABC is an isosceles triangle. Find ∠e.

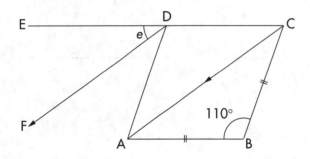

(6) ABCD is a rectangle. ABEF is a parallelogram. Find ∠f.

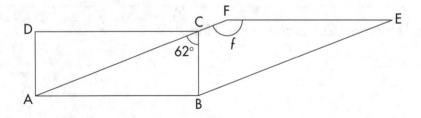

(7) △ABC is an equilateral triangle. DCE // BAF. Find ∠g.

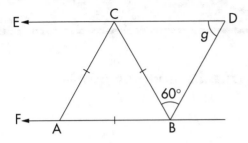

(8) △ABC is an isosceles triangle. ABD // EF. Find ∠h.

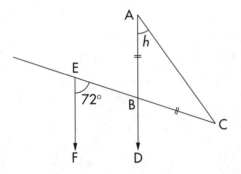

(9) ABCD is a rectangle. CDEF is a square. Find ∠i.

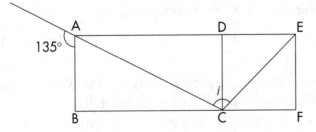

A. Choose the correct answer and write its number in the parentheses provided.

(1) Find the value of $\frac{7}{10} \div 7$.

    (1) $\frac{5}{12}$ (2) $\frac{1}{10}$ (3) $\frac{2}{7}$ (4) $\frac{2}{3}$ (   )

(2) Express 600 ml as a percentage of 3 ℓ.
    (1) 0.2%   (2) 2%   (3) 20%   (4) 22%   (   )

(3) 45% = _____

    (1) $\frac{9}{20}$ (2) $\frac{7}{10}$ (3) $\frac{3}{5}$ (4) $\frac{1}{4}$ (   )

(4) 20 out of 60 = ?

    (1) $\frac{1}{5}$ (2) $\frac{1}{4}$ (3) $\frac{1}{3}$ (4) $\frac{1}{2}$ (   )

(5) 15 : ☐ : 9 = 5 : 2 : 3
    (1) 3   (2) 4   (3) 5   (4) 6   (   )

(6) 7 : 4 = ☐ : 16. The missing number in the box is _____.
    (1) 112   (2) 64   (3) 49   (4) 28   (   )

(7) There are 15 one-dollar bills and 9 five-dollar bills in my pocket. What is the ratio of the number of one-dollar bills to the number of five-dollar bills?
    (1) 3 : 15   (2) 5 : 3   (3) 5 : 9   (4) 9 : 15   (   )

(8) In a school cafeteria, there are 5 boys to every 4 girls. If there are 40 girls, how many boys are there?
    (1) 8 boys   (2) 10 boys   (3) 20 boys   (4) 50 boys   (   )

(9) Write $\frac{7}{20}$ as a percentage.

    (1) 20%   (2) 35%   (3) 70%   (4) 140%   (   )

(10) 1.5% is the same as _____.

    (1) 150   (2) 15   (3) 0.15   (4) 0.015   (   )

(11) There are 2 pineapples. Pineapple A weighs 2 kg. Pineapple B weighs 1 kg 500 g. Express pineapple B's weight as a percentage of pineapple A's weight.

    (1) 750%   (2) 75%   (3) 0.75%   (4) 7.5%   (   )

(12) Find the perimeter of this figure made up of two semicircles and a rectangle. (Take $\pi = \frac{22}{7}$.)

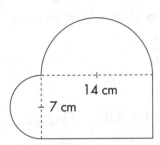

    (1) 54 cm
    (2) 56 cm
    (3) 57 cm
    (4) 59 cm   (   )

(13) In the figure below, the ratio of the area of the square to the area of the rectangle is _____.

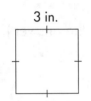
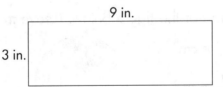

    (1) 1 : 3
    (2) 2 : 7
    (3) 3 : 5
    (4) 9 : 3   (   )

(14) Find the area of the shaded part of this figure. (Take $\pi = 3.14$.)

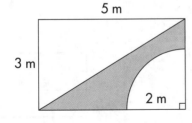

    (1) 7.51 m^2
    (2) 4.36 m^2
    (3) 3.14 m^2
    (4) 2.28 m^2 (   )

(15) Find the perimeter of this figure made up of three semicircles. (Take $\pi = \frac{22}{7}$.)

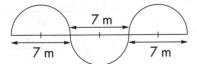

    (1) 21 m   (2) 32 m
    (3) 43 m   (4) 54 m   (   )

(16) Find the circumference of the circle below correct to 2 decimal places.
(Take π = 3.14.)

    (1) 6.28 cm   (2) 4.08 cm

    (3) 2.04 cm   (4) 1.33 cm   (   )

(17) Mark bought 3 kg 600 g of cookies. He ate 85% of it. How many grams of cookies were left over?

    (1) 3600 g   (2) 3060 g   (3) 850 g   (4) 540 g (   )

(18) A train could travel $60\frac{1}{2}$ km in $\frac{1}{4}$ hour. It traveled at this speed for $\frac{7}{10}$ h and covered half the distance of its journey. Find the distance of its whole journey.

    (1) 338.8 km   (2) 438.8 km

    (3) 328.8 km   (4) 383.8 km   (   )

(19) Charles bought 2 kg of fish for $\$20\frac{1}{2}$ and 4 kg of beef for $\$40\frac{1}{2}$. Find the difference in price between one kilogram of each type of meat.

    (1) $\$\frac{1}{10}$ (2) $\$\frac{1}{8}$ (3) $\$\frac{1}{6}$ (4) $\$\frac{1}{4}$ (   )

(20) Find the area of the shaded part of the figure below. (Leave π in the answer.)

    (1) $12\frac{1}{3}$ π cm²   (2) $18\frac{3}{4}$ π cm²

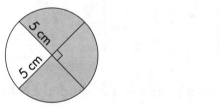

    (3) $22\frac{2}{3}$ π cm²   (4) $28\frac{1}{4}$ π cm²   (   )

B. Fill in the blanks.

(1) Write 0.046 as a percentage.

                                              %

(2) 25% of 300 ml = _____

                                            ml

(3) $\frac{3}{5}$ = _____

                                            %

(4) Linda shared a bag of candy with Lindsey in the ratio of
     3 : 7. Express Lindsey's share as a fraction of Linda's share.

(5) Find the area of the circle below. (Take π = $\frac{22}{7}$.)

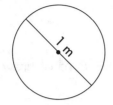

m²

(6) 10 journals out of 50 were graded. What percentage
     of journals were not graded?

%

(7) Larry jogged around a circular field. The diameter of the field
     was 35 m. The distance covered was 1100 m. How many

     rounds did he jog? (Take π = $\frac{22}{7}$.)

rounds

(8) What percentage of 3.5 km is 500 m?

%

(9) The cost price of a cassette player was $185. It was sold
     for $194.25. What was the percentage profit?

%

(10) Find the area of the shaded part. (Take π = 3.14)

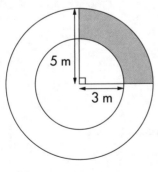

m²

(11) I had $6.30. I spent $\frac{5}{9}$ of it on a movie ticket. How much
     money did I have left?

$

(12) Cameron scored 75 points for the second test and 90 points
     for the third test. The percentage increase in points was

     _____.

%

(13) $\left(\dfrac{3}{5} - \dfrac{1}{10}\right) \div \dfrac{5}{2} =$

(14) $\left(2 + \dfrac{1}{2}\right) \div \left(\dfrac{2}{3} + 1\right) + \dfrac{2}{3} \times \dfrac{9}{4} =$

(15) Pam has a small pickup truck that can carry $\dfrac{2}{3}$ cord of firewood. Find the number of trips needed to deliver 40 cords of wood.

(16) The human body contains 90 pounds of water for every 100 pounds of body weight. How many pounds of water are in a child who weighs 80 pounds?

(17) A batch of double chocolate chip cookies requires $\dfrac{1}{4}$ pound of chocolate chips. If you have 3 pounds of chocolate chips, how many batches of cookies can be made?

(18) Express 30 cups as a fraction of 9 gallons.

C. Do these problems. Show all your work clearly.

(1) The average speed of trains A and B is 62 km/h. If the average speed of train A is 60 km/h, what will be the time taken for train B to complete a journey of 320 km?

(2) Ranjit left $72, 000 to be shared among his wife and 3 sons in the ratio 4 : 6. If the sons were to get equal shares, how much did each of them receive?

(3) There were 3 pieces of string, A, B and C. String A was $2\frac{1}{5}$ m longer than string C. String B was $1\frac{1}{2}$ m shorter than string A. Find the average length of the three pieces of string if string C was $\frac{9}{10}$ m.

(4) The diagram below shows a fence made of iron bars. The curved parts are semicircular in shape. What is the length of iron bars needed to construct the fence? (Take $\pi = 3.14$)

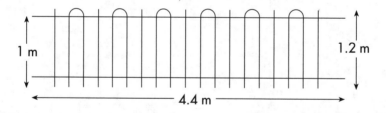

A. Choose the correct answer and write its number in the parentheses provided.

The pie chart below shows the percentages of the different types of spectators at a volleyball match. There are 120 spectators altogether. Use the pie chart to answer questions 1 to 3.

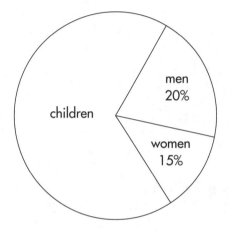

(1) What percentage of the spectators are children?
 (1) 45%   (2) 55%   (3) 65%   (4) 75%   (   )

(2) How many women are there?
 (1) 18   (2) 24   (3) 36   (4) 42   (   )

(3) What fraction of the spectators are men?

 (1) $\dfrac{3}{20}$ (2) $\dfrac{1}{5}$ (3) $\dfrac{13}{21}$ (4) $\dfrac{15}{17}$ (   )

(4) In the figure below which is not drawn to scale, ABCD is a parallelogram. △BEF is an isosceles triangle. Find ∠b.

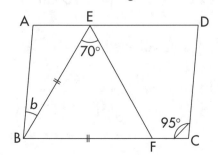

 (1) 25°
 (2) 30°
 (3) 35°
 (4) 45°   (   )

(5) In the figure below which is not drawn to scale, ABCD is a trapezoid. Find ∠d.

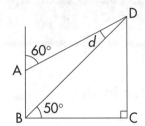

    (1) 10°
    (2) 15°
    (3) 20°
    (4) 30°   (   )

(6) In the figure below which is not drawn to scale, ABCD is a square and △ADE is an equilateral triangle. Find ∠c.

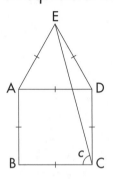

    (1) 45°
    (2) 55°
    (3) 65°
    (4) 75°   (   )

(7) Find the value of $30 + g$ if $g = 5$.
    (1) 25   (2) 35   (3) 45   (4) 55   (   )

(8) When $b = 3$, the value of $5b - b$ is _____.
    (1) 18   (2) 16   (3) 12   (4) 10   (   )

(9) A rectangular tin 15 cm by 11 cm by 7 cm is 30% filled with cooking oil. How many liters of cooking oil are there in the tin? Give your answer correct to 2 decimal places. (1 ℓ = 1000 cm³)
    (1) 0.35   (2) 0.36   (3) 0.37   (4) 0.38   (   )

(10) A tank measuring 60 cm long and 40 cm wide is $\frac{3}{5}$ full of water. If the water in the tank is 28,800 cm³, find the height of the tank.
    (1) 20 cm   (2) 22 cm   (3) 24 cm   (4) 25 cm (   )

(11) The solid below is made up of 2-cm cubes. What is its volume?

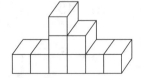

    (1) 36 cm³   (2) 72 cm³
    (3) 84 cm³   (4) 90 cm³ (   )

(12) A rectangular tank 20 cm by 15 cm by 10 cm was $\frac{3}{5}$ full of water. 0.5 ℓ of water was poured away. How many milliliters of water were left over? (1 ℓ = 1000 cm³)

   (1) 1300 ml   (2) 1305 ml   (3) 1350 ml   (4) 1530 ml (   )

(13) Amy has 3 times as much money as her sister. If her sister has \$5d, how much does Amy have?

   (1) \$$\frac{3}{5}d$ (2) \$2.5d   (3) \$1$\frac{2}{3}d$ (4) \$15d   (   )

B.   Fill in the boxes with the correct answers.

(1)   In the figure below which is not drawn to scale, ABCD is a rhombus.
$\angle m$ = _____.

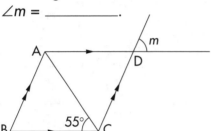

(2)   In the figure below which is not drawn to scale, ABCD is a rectangle and △ADE is an isosceles triangle.
$\angle d$ = _____.

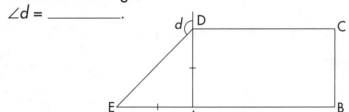

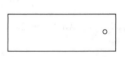

(3)   In the figure below which is not drawn to scale, ABCD and CDEF are parallelograms.
$\angle c$ = _____.

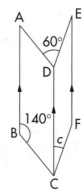

(4) Mrs. Wang had \$2.10. She gave $\frac{1}{6}$ of it to her son and $\frac{2}{7}$ to her daughter. How much money did she give away altogether?

$\quad$ \$ _____

(5) When $S = 6$, the value of $\frac{5}{S} + S^2$ is _____.

$\quad$ _____

(6) Simplify $6m + 5 - 2m$ and the answer is _____.

$\quad$ _____

(7) The solid below is made up of 2 cm cubes. Its volume is _____.

$\quad$ _____ cm^3

(8) 35 out of 70 = _____.

$\quad$ _____ %

(9) $\frac{3}{7}$ of the eggs in a basket is 24 eggs. What is the total number of eggs in the basket?

$\quad$ _____ eggs

(10) Jamie's age is $\frac{2}{f}$ of her father's. The ratio of her age to her father's age is _____.

$\quad$ _____

(11) The volume of a cuboid a cm long and b cm wide is d cm³. Its height is _____.

$\quad$ _____ cm

(12) A shopkeeper had $24p$ lb of sugar. He divided it equally into small bags. Each bag contained $6p$ lb of sugar. How many bags were there?

$\quad$ _____ bags

C. Do these problems. Show all your work clearly.

(1) A wooden cuboid measures 10 cm long, 8 cm wide and 6 cm high. If a cube of side 4 cm is cut off from it, what is the volume of the remaining block of wood?

(2) A rectangular tank 25 cm long, 20 cm wide and 8 cm high holds 2500 cm^3 of water. When a stone is put into it, the height of the water rises to 7 cm. Find the volume of the stone.

(3)   The Murray family is making three kinds of holiday cookies that require brown sugar. The recipes call for $2\frac{1}{4}$ cups, $1\frac{1}{2}$ cups and $\frac{3}{4}$ cups. They bought two packages of brown sugar, each holding $2\frac{1}{3}$ cups. How much more (or less) is the amount of sugar bought than the amount needed?

(4)   Jessica has a roll of cloth which is 9 yards long. She cut off 12 pieces, each $1\frac{1}{2}$ feet. She cut off another piece that was 2 feet 10 inches long. What is the length of the remaining piece of cloth?

A. **Each question is followed by four answers. Choose the correct answer and write its number in the parentheses provided. (40 points)**

(1) Reduce $\frac{126}{315}$ to its simplest form.

    (1) $\frac{2}{3}$ (2) $\frac{3}{4}$ (3) $\frac{1}{5}$ (4) $\frac{2}{5}$ (   )

(2) How many grams are there in 7.32 kg?
    (1) 73,200 g   (2) 7320 g   (3) 732 g   (4) 73.2 g (   )

(3) Express 50 min as a fraction of 1 h 15 min.

    (1) $\frac{1}{7}$ (2) $\frac{2}{3}$ (3) $\frac{3}{4}$ (4) $\frac{5}{6}$ (   )

(4) 65% = _____

    (1) $\frac{5}{6}$ (2) $\frac{7}{12}$ (3) $\frac{13}{20}$ (4) $\frac{12}{23}$ (   )

(5) There are 50 passengers in a hall. 15 of them are women. What percent are **not** women?
    (1) 70%   (2) 68%   (3) 50%   (4) 15%   (   )

(6) Simplify $1 \times 1^2 \times 1^3$.
    (1) 0.01   (2) 1   (3) 3   (4) 10   (   )

(7) The area of a square is 81 cm². What is the perimeter of the square?
    (1) 63 cm   (2) 52 cm   (3) 49 cm   (4) 36 cm (   )

(8) Suren saves $15 in two months. At this rate, how much can he save in a year?
    (1) $36   (2) $54   (3) $90   (4) $102   (   )

(9) The distance from city A to city B is 330 mi. A car leaves city A at 8 a.m. and travels at a uniform speed of 50 mi/h. At what time will it reach city B?
    (1) 2:36 p.m.   (2) 2:26 p.m.   (3) 2:16 p.m.   (4) 2:06 p.m.(   )

(10) $4 : \boxed{} = 28 : 63$. What is the missing number in the box?

    (1) 11   (2) 9   (3) 7   (4) 5   (   )

(11) I have 16 nickels, 10 quarters and 24 dimes. The ratio of the number of quarters to the number of dimes to the number of nickels is _____.

    (1) 8 : 5 : 12   (2) 5 : 8 : 12
    (3) 12 : 5 : 8   (4) 5 : 12 : 8   (   )

(12) Find the value of $\dfrac{40 - x}{12}$ if $x = 4$.

    (1) 3   (2) 4   (3) 5   (4) 6   (   )

(13) A boy buys 4 pencils at q ¢ each and has 50¢ left. How much does he have at first?

    (1) $(50 + 4q)$¢   (2) $(q + 54)$¢
    (3) $(4q + 50)$¢   (4) $(54q)$¢   (   )

(14) In the figure, find the total area of the **unshaded** parts.

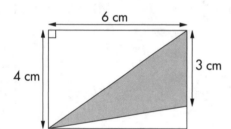

    (1) 6 cm²   (2) 9 cm²

    (3) $10\frac{1}{2}$ cm²   (4) 15 cm² (   )

(15) A piece of board 8 yd by 6 yd is cut into squares. The perimeter of each square is 8 yd. How many squares are there?

    (1) 14   (2) 12   (3) 10   (4) 8   (   )

(16) Find the volume of the solid below.

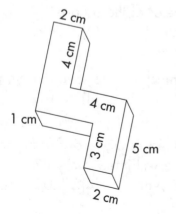

    (1) 14 cm³
    (2) 16 cm³
    (3) 18 cm³
    (4) 26 cm³   (   )

The graph below shows the number of schools built in Town S from 1981 to 1984. Use it to answer questions 17 and 18.

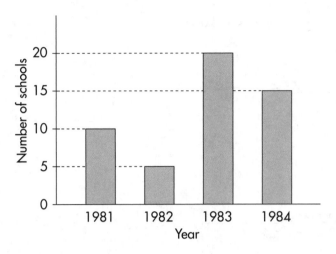

(17) In which year was the greatest number of schools built?
    (1) 1981   (2) 1982   (3) 1983   (4) 1984   (   )

(18) What was the total number of schools built from 1981 to 1984?
    (1) 15   (2) 20   (3) 35   (4) 50   (   )

(19) In the figure below which is not drawn to scale, find the value of $\angle a + \angle c$.

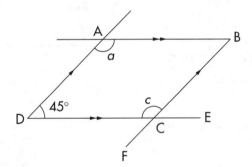

    (1) $45°$
    (2) $135°$
    (3) $270°$
    (4) $360°$ (   )

(20) Which solid can be formed by the given net?

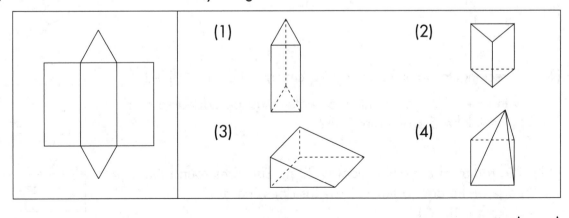

                                    (   )

B. **Write the correct answers in the boxes provided. (24 points)**

(1) $10 \times \frac{1}{2} \times (\frac{5}{8} + \frac{7}{4} - \frac{3}{8}) \div 4 + 10 =$ _____

☐

(2) $6 + \frac{7}{10} +$ _____ $+ \frac{5}{1000} = 6.735$

☐

(3) $2\frac{3}{4}h =$ _____

☐ min

(4) 85% of 1 ℓ 300 ml = _____

☐ ml

(5) Josh bought 2 lb 8 oz of beef and 8 oz of pork. Express the weight of the pork as a percentage of the weight of the beef.

☐ %

(6) The average income of Curly, Larry and Mo is $958. Larry earns $895 and Mo earns $975. How much does Curly earn?

$ ☐

(7) Paula spent $545 to cement a square piece of ground at $5.45 per m². What is the area of the ground?

☐ m²

(8) The ratio of the area of a square to the area of a rectangle is 3 : 5. Express this as a fraction.

☐

(9) $\frac{27}{28} \div \frac{21}{16} =$ _____

☐

(10) A rectangular tank 10 cm by 20 cm by 30 cm is $\frac{3}{4}$ filled with water. How many liters of water must be added so that there will be 5 ℓ of water in it?

☐ ℓ

(11) The radius of a circular pool is 20 m. Lisa runs round the edge of the pool 5 times. How far does she run? (Take π = 3.14.)

☐ m

(12) In the figure below which is not drawn to scale, ∠ABC = 90°. Find ∠x.

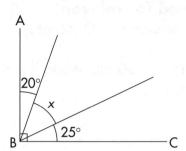

∠x = [   ] °

C. Show how the following shape can tessellate in the space provided by drawing 5 more unit shapes. (6 points)

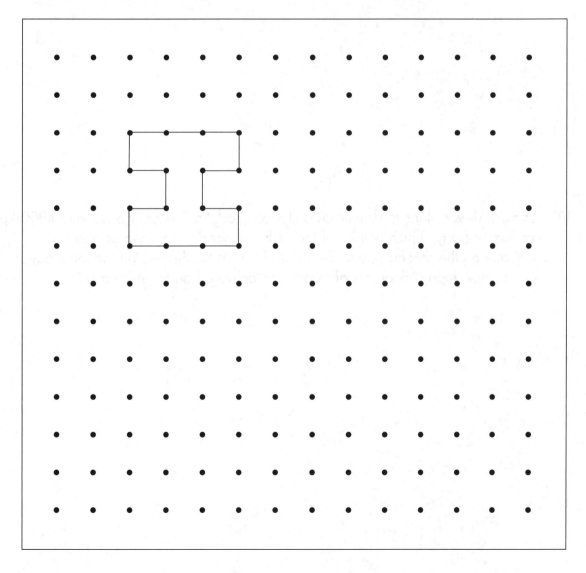

D. Answer each question in the space provided. Your work must be clearly shown as points will be awarded for relevant mathematical statements and the correct answer. (30 points)

(1) Osman bought a calculator and 5 cassettes. He paid $62.50 altogether. If the calculator cost $25, how much did each cassette cost?

(2) A truck driver plans to deliver an order of goods in 3 days. He delivers 4800 kg on the first day, which is 40% of the order of goods. The ratio of goods he delivers on the second day to the ratio of goods he delivers on the third day is 3 : 5. How many kilograms of goods are delivered on the third day?

(3) The average height of Samy, Gomez, Siti and David is 1.2 m. The average height of Samy and Gomez is 1.25 m. What is the total height of Siti and David?

(4) The ratio of the weight of oil in barrel A to the weight of oil in barrel B is 4 : 3. If $\frac{1}{3}$ of the oil in barrel A is poured into barrel B, the oil in barrel B will be heavier than the oil in barrel A by 15 kg. How much oil is in barrel A? Give your answer in kilograms.

(5) Liming drove at an average speed of 60 km/h for $2\frac{1}{2}$ h and then stopped for 10 minutes to have her lunch. After lunch, she covered the rest of the journey at a speed of 50 km/h. If the total distance she traveled was 225 km, how long did she take for the whole journey?

GENERAL REVIEW 2

A. Each question is followed by four answers. Choose the correct answer and write its number in the parentheses provided. (40 points)

(1) Which of the following is the common factor of 12 and 15?
    (1) 7   (2) 5   (3) 3   (4) 2   (   )

(2) Express $5 as a percentage of $80.
    (1) $6\frac{2}{3}\%$ (2) $6\frac{1}{4}\%$ (3) $6\frac{4}{5}\%$ (4) $6\frac{1}{6}\%$ (   )

(3) A man works 8 hours each day and is paid $y an hour. If he works 6 days a week, what is his weekly income?
    (1) $(48y)$ (2) $(48 - y)$ (3) $(8 + y)$ (4) $(y + 48)$(   )

(4) The ratio of Lisa's savings to David's savings was 4 : 7. Lisa saved $32. How much did David save?
    (1) $40   (2) $48   (3) $52   (4) $56   (   )

(5) A person bicycled 4500 m in 15 min. What was his average speed in kilometers per hour?
    (1) 16 km/h   (2) 18 km/h   (3) 22 km/h   (4) 28 km/h(   )

(6) The water from a leaking tap drips into a bucket at the rate of 0.05 ℓ per minute. How much water will be collected in the bucket in 1 h 15 min?
    (1) 1.55 ℓ (2) 2.25 ℓ (3) 3.75 ℓ (4) 4.05 ℓ (   )

(7) The average weight of 4 bags of sugar is 725 g. Their total weight is _____.
    (1) 2 kg 9 g   (2) 2 kg 10 g
    (3) 2 kg 90 g   (4) 2 kg 900 g   (   )

(8) Mary had 2.5 ℓ of fresh milk. She gave 500 ml to each of her three friends and kept the rest for herself. How much fresh milk did she have?
    (1) 0.1 ℓ (2) 0.5 ℓ (3) 1 ℓ (4) 1.5 ℓ (   )

(9) Which of the following is true?
    (1) $0.1 \times 0.1 = 0.001$ (2) $0.1 \times 0.1 = 1$
    (3) $0.1 \times 0.1 = 0.01$ (4) $0.1 \times 0.1 = 0.1$ (   )

(10) 25% of 50 kg is

(1) $12\frac{1}{2}$ kg   (2) $15\frac{1}{5}$ kg   (3) 25 kg   (4) $25\frac{1}{2}$ kg (   )

(11) The figure shows a solid that is made up of unit cubes. At least how many unit cubes are needed to add onto the solid to form a cuboid?

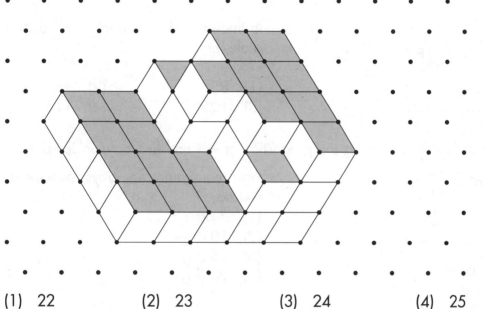

(1) 22   (2) 23   (3) 24   (4) 25   (   )

(12) Which of the following is equal to 5%?
(1) 5   (2) 0.5   (3) 0.05   (4) 0.005 (   )

(13) 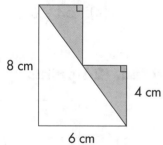 In the figure, find the total area of the shaded parts.

(1) 12 cm²
(2) 24 cm²
(3) 32 cm²
(4) 48 cm²   (   )

(14) 3450 ml = _____
(1) 0.345 ℓ (2) 3.45 ℓ (3) 34.5 ℓ (4) 345 ℓ (   )

(15) A rectangular tank 40 cm long, 25 cm wide and 30 cm high is filled with water. If 5 ℓ of water is poured out, what is the drop in the water level? (1 ℓ = 1000 cm³)
(1) 2 cm   (2) 3 cm   (3) 4 cm   (4) 5 cm   (   )

(16) In the figure below which is not drawn to scale, AB and CD are straight lines.
$\angle m = $ _____

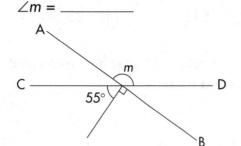

(1) 115°
(2) 125°
(3) 135°
(4) 145°   (   )

(17)

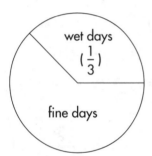

In the figure below which is not drawn to scale, find $\angle n$.

(1) 85°   (2) 95°
(3) 105°   (4) 115°   (   )

(18) The pie chart below shows the proportion of wet and fine days in June.

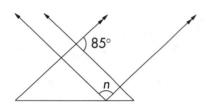

wet days $(\frac{1}{3})$

fine days

How many more fine days were there than wet days?
(1) 3 days
(2) 10 days
(3) 15 days
(4) 20 days   (   )

(19) The square of 8 has the same value as the cube of _____.
(1) 3   (2) 4   (3) 5   (4) 6   (   )

(20) 35 out of 75 is the same as _____.
(1) $2\frac{1}{7}\%$ (2) $31\frac{3}{4}\%$ (3) $46\frac{2}{3}\%$ (4) $54\frac{4}{5}\%$ (   )

B. Write the correct answers in the boxes provided. (24 points)

(1) Express 0.08 as a fraction in its simplest form.

(2) The marked price of a digital watch was $25. Peiyi bought it for $20. The discount given was _____.

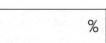
%

(3) The ages of Laura, Mary and Sally are 12 years, 4 years and 20 years respectively. The ratio of Mary's age to Laura's age to Sally's age is _____.

(4) A pick-up travels at a speed of 40 km/h. What distance will it travel in $3\frac{3}{4}$ hours?

km

(5) I have $\frac{5}{7}$ as many stamps as my sister has. The ratio of the number of my stamps to the number of my sister's stamps is _____.

(6) 0.85 = _____

%

(7) How many dots can I draw on the circumference of a circular figure 14 cm in diameter, if the dots are drawn 2 cm apart along the circumference? (Take $\pi = \frac{22}{7}$.)

dots

(8) In the figure, find the volume of the shaded portion.

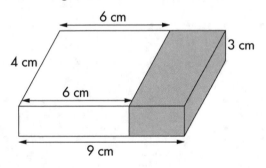

cm³

(9) In the figure not drawn to scale, $\angle p =$ _____.

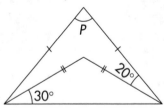

°

(10) In the figure not drawn to scale, $\angle y =$ _____.

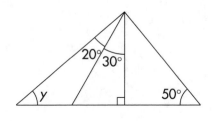

°

(11) When 3051 is divided by 24, the remainder is _____.

(12) May had 1 lb of wheat flour. She gave $\frac{2}{5}$ of it to Peter and $\frac{1}{3}$ of it to Bill. What fraction of the wheat flour did she have left?

C. Show how the following shape can tessellate in the space provided by drawing 5 more unit shapes. (6 points)

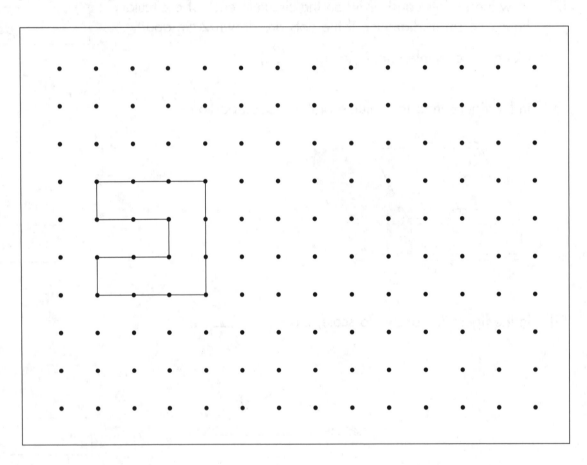

D. **Answer each question in the space provided. Your work must be clearly shown as points will be awarded for relevant mathematical statements and the correct answer. (30 points)**

(1) After spending 0.3 of his money on a pocket dictionary and 0.25 of the remainder on a book, Jerry had $5.25 left. How much did he have to start with?

(2) Rosa has 2 lb 4 oz of beef less than Steven. Steven has 1 lb 13 oz of beef more than Maria. Maria has 4 lb 5 oz of beef. How much more beef does Maria have than Rosa?

(3)   The ratio of the perimeter of a square to the perimeter of a rectangle is 1 : 2. If the rectangle is 14 ft long and 10 ft wide, find the area of the square.

(4)   David has 342 stamps, Jed has 294 stamps and Paul has 225 stamps. How many stamps must David and Jed give to Paul altogether so that they will each have the same number of stamps?

(5)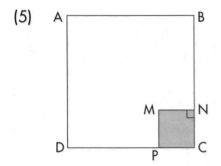

In the figure, the area of square ABCD is 100 cm² and the area of square MNCP is 9 cm². Find the length of BN.

A. **Each question is followed by four answers. Choose the correct answer and write its number in the parentheses provided. (40 points)**

(1) The value of $6 + 5 \times 3 - 8 \div 4$ is _____.
    (1) 19   (2) 17   (3) 15   (4) 13   (   )

(2) Simplify $1\frac{1}{4} - \frac{9}{10} \div \frac{2}{3} \div 3$.
    (1) 0.77   (2) 0.78   (3) 0.79   (4) 0.8   (   )

(3) Find the value of $\frac{3}{4}$ of 1 km 200 m.
    (1) 0.9 km   (2) 0.8 km   (3) 0.7 km   (4) 0.6 km (   )

(4) How many years and months are there in $2\frac{5}{6}$ years?
    (1) 2 years 5 months   (2) 2 years 6 months
    (3) 2 years 10 months   (4) 2 years 11 months   (   )

(5) Which of the following has the greatest value?
    (1) 1   (2) 0.98   (3) $\frac{124}{125}$ (4) 85%   (   )

(6) There are 44 students in a class. 75% of them passed the Mathematics test. How many students did **not** pass the Mathematics test?
    (1) 11   (2) 24   (3) 33   (4) 40   (   )

(7) The area of one face of a cube is 9 in.^{2}. The volume of the cube is _____.
    (1) 18 in.^{3} (2) 27 in.^{3} (3) 81 in.^{3} (4) 729 in.^{3} (   )

(8) Gopal is 12 years 9 months old. His twin sisters are each 8 years 6 months old. What is the average age of the three children?
    (1) 8 years 7 months   (2) 9 years 9 months
    (3) 9 years 11 months   (4) 10 years 2 months   (   )

(9) A wheel makes 5000 revolutions in $\frac{1}{3}$ h. How many revolutions does it make in 1 h 10 min?
    (1) 14,300   (2) 15,500   (3) 16,400   (4) 17,500 (   )

(10) In the figure below, find the ratio of the length of AB to the perimeter of the triangle.

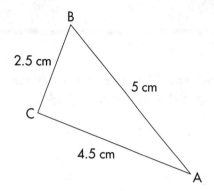

(1) 1 : 2
(2) 5 : 12
(3) 2 : 3
(4) 6 : 7   (   )

(11) Find the value of $\dfrac{m}{m^2} + m$ when $m = 7$.

(1) $49\dfrac{1}{7}$ (2) $17\dfrac{1}{49}$ (3) $7\dfrac{3}{14}$ (4) $7\dfrac{1}{7}$ (   )

(12) Mrs. Feng bought m kg of rice. She used 2 kg of it a day. How much rice would be left after 2 weeks?
(1) $14(m - 2)$ kg   (2) $(28 - m)$ kg
(3) $(m - 28)$ kg   (4) $(m - 14)$ kg   (   )

(13) The postage rates for sending packages to Canada are $10.50 for the first 10 oz and $2.80 for every additional 10 oz or part thereof. How much will Mr. Han have to pay for a package which weighs 1 lb 6 oz?
(1) $14.20   (2) $15.10   (3) $15.40   (4) $16.10 (   )

(14) In the figure below, find the area of the shaded part. (Take $\pi = \dfrac{22}{7}$.)

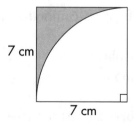

7 cm

7 cm

(1) $10\dfrac{1}{2}$ cm²
(2) 14 cm²
(3) $49\dfrac{1}{2}$ cm²
(4) 154 cm²   (   )

114

(15) Which solid can be formed by the given net?

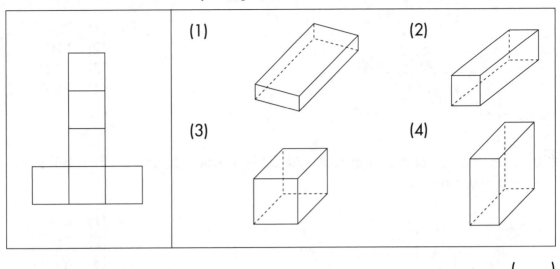

( )

(16) How many wooden blocks 2 cm by 2 cm by 2 cm will fill this box?

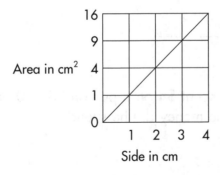

(1) 125
(2) 150
(3) 175
(4) 200   (   )

The graph below shows the relation between the sides and the areas of squares. Use it to answer questions 17 and 18.

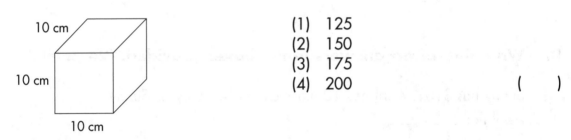

(17) What is the area of a square of side 2 cm?
(1) 1 cm² (2) 4 cm² (3) 9 cm² (4) 16 cm² (   )

(18) The area of a square is 16 cm². The side of the square is _____.
(1) 1 cm (2) 2 cm (3) 3 cm (4) 4 cm (   )

(19) In the figure not drawn to scale, what is the value of ∠q?

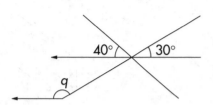

(1) 70°
(2) 110°
(3) 140°
(4) 150°   (   )

(20) In the figure not drawn to scale, ABCD is a rectangle and △CEF is an isosceles triangle. Find ∠e.

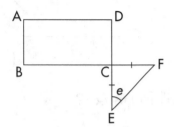

(1) 45°
(2) 54°
(3) 60°
(4) 90°   (   )

B. Write the correct answers in the boxes provided. (24 points)

(1) Sunny has $101. April has 10 times as much money as Sunny. April has _____.

$ [   ]

(2) Round off 5.163 to the nearest whole number. The answer is _____.

[   ]

(3) $\frac{2}{3} + \frac{2}{3} + \frac{2}{3} = \frac{2}{3} \times$ _____.

[   ]

(4) Austin had $7.80. He spent $4 on a pen and $3.80 on a doll. What percentage of the money did he spend?

[   ] %

(5) $m + 2m \times \frac{1}{2} =$ _____.

[   ]

(6) The average of three numbers is 36. A fourth number is 48. The average of the four numbers is _____.

[   ]

116

(7) Miss Xie drove a car to the university which was 80 mi away. She left her house at 7:10 a.m. and reached the university at 8:30 a.m. Her average speed was _____.

(8) Rosalina and Kris shared 2.5 lb of milk powder in the ratio of 2 : 3. How much milk powder did Kris get?

lb

(9) $0.35 \times 21.7 =$ _____.

(10) In the figure not drawn to scale, ABGH and CDEF are rectangles. BCFG is a parallelogram. $\angle f$ is _____.

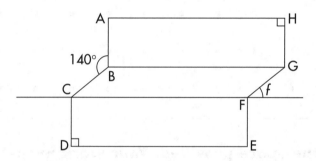

(11) In the figure below which is not drawn to scale, $\angle g$ is _____.

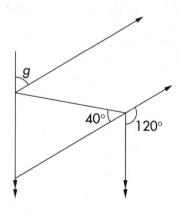

(12) A rectangular block 6 cm by 2 cm by 10 cm is cut away from a wooden cube of side 10 cm. The volume of wood that is left is _____.

cm³

C. **The figure shows half of a symmetrical figure. The dotted line is a line of symmetry. Complete the symmetrical figure. (6 points)**

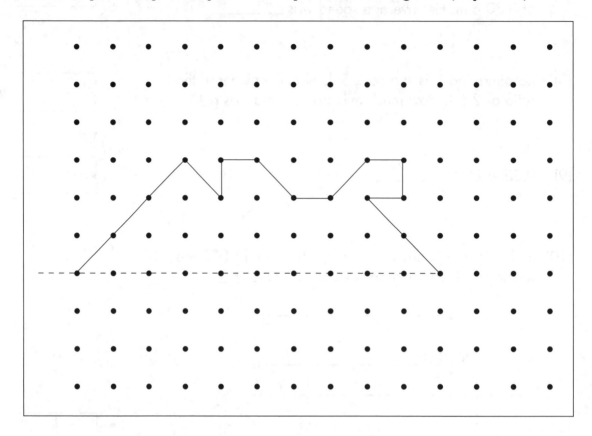

D. **Answer each question in the space provided. Your work must be clearly shown as points will be awarded for relevant mathematical statements and the correct answer. (30 points)**

(1) A shopkeeper bought 300 apples for $60. 10% of the apples were rotten. He sold the rest at $1 for 3. How much profit did he make?

(2)   The ratio of John's English test points to those of Sam and Lisa is 2 : 3 : 4.
      If Sam scores 66 points, what is the difference between John's and Lisa's points?

(3)   The students in a class are divided into 2 teams. The ratio of the number of
      students in Team A to that in Team B is 5 : 3. If 14 students from Team A join
      Team B, the ratio becomes 1 : 2. How many students are there in each team at
      first?

(4) A rectangular tank 50 cm by 40 cm by 10 cm is $\frac{3}{5}$ filled with water. If the water is poured equally into 6 smaller containers, how many liters of water does each container hold? (1 ℓ = 1000 cm³)

(5) A circular pond of diameter 10 m has a 1 m wide cement path all round. Find the total cost of the cement path if each m² of cementing costs $7.50. (Take π = 3.14.)

ANSWERS

Exercise 1

(1) (a) $(x + 53)$ (b) $58   (c) $63

(2) (a) $\dfrac{24}{y}$ (b) 8   (c) 6

(3) (a) $(m - 2.50)$ (b) $7.50   (c) $3

(4) (a) $5L$ cm²   (b) 40 cm²   (c) 60 cm²

(5) (a) $12(S - 1500)$ (b) $9600   (c) $15,600

(6) (a) $\left(\dfrac{N}{5} - 100\right)$ g   (b) 1200 g   (c) 1700 g

Exercise 2

A   (1) 7   (2) 28   (3) 100   (4) 5
     (5) 4   (6) 9   (7) 80   (8) 25

B   (1) 45   (2) 35   (3) 1   (4) 3
     (5) 105   (6) 192   (7) 11   (8) 10

C   (1) $2m$ (2) $3N$ (3) $6p$ (4) $9q$
     (5) $5b$ (6) $12a$ (7) $7g$ (8) $8e$
     (9) $10z - 5$ (10) $5t - 6$ (11) $f - 6$
     (12) $8d + 1$ (13) $3 + 2a$ (14) $2h + 2$
     (15) $8k$ (16) $15 - r$

Exercise 3

(1) (a) 6   (b) 5   (c) 3   (d) 5

(2) b, c (3) a, d (4) b (5) b

Exercise 4

(1) (a) 2 : 3   (b) 3 : 2

(2) (a) 7 : 10 : 4   (b) 10 : 21

(3) (a) $\dfrac{4}{5}$ (b) $\dfrac{5}{9}$

(4) (a) $\dfrac{7}{3}$ (b) $\dfrac{3}{7}$ (c) $\dfrac{7}{10}$

(5) (a) 5 : 6   (b) 3   (c) $\dfrac{1}{2}$

(6) (a) 2 : 3   (b) $\dfrac{3}{2}$

(7) 12   (8) 24 cm   (9) 27, 18, 45

(10) (a) 4 : 5   (b) 125

(11) $14\dfrac{1}{2}$ kg   (12) 900 m²

Exercise 5

(1) 30   (2) 50 g

(3) $12\dfrac{8}{9}$ cm, $9\dfrac{2}{3}$ cm, $6\dfrac{4}{9}$ cm

(4) 160 cm   (5) 52   (6) 140

Exercise 6

(1) 5 : 2   (2) $25   (3) 40

(4) 600   (5) 140 m

(6) Team A: 210,   Team B: 90

Exercise 7

A   (1) $37\dfrac{1}{2}$%   (2) 44%   (3) 38%   (4) 60%

B   (1) 25%   (2) 40%   (3) $62\dfrac{1}{2}$%

C   (1) 32%   (2) 10%   (3) 20%   (4) $37\dfrac{1}{2}$%
     (5) 80%   (6) $12\dfrac{1}{2}$%   (7) 40%   (8) 60%

D   (1) $\dfrac{1}{25}$ (2) $\dfrac{2}{25}$ (3) $\dfrac{17}{100}$ (4) $\dfrac{3}{10}$
     (5) $\dfrac{73}{100}$ (6) $\dfrac{4}{5}$ (7) $\dfrac{99}{100}$ (8) 1

E   (1) 50%   (2) 1%   (3) 26%   (4) 48%
     (5) 1.2%   (6) 0.7%   (7) 40.3%   (8) 39.1%

F   (1) 0.03   (2) 0.06   (3) 0.07   (4) 0.29
     (5) 0.33   (6) 0.56   (7) 0.7   (8) 0.9

Exercise 8

(1) 20%   (2) 40%   (3) 50%   (4) 75%

(5) 60%   (6) 25%   (7) 18%   (8) 8%

(9) 16%   (10) 49%   (11) 20%   (12) 15%

Exercise 9

(1) 8%   (2) 52%   (3) 30%   (4) 32%

(5) 25%   (6) 160%   (7) 20%   (8) 120%

(9) 270%   (10) 40%

Exercise 10

(1) $15.60   (2) $646   (3) 36

(4) 94.5 kg   (5) $9\dfrac{1}{11}$%   (6) $2662.50

(7) 1750   (8) $40   (9) 300

(10) $1050   (11) 60   (12) 24

Exercise 11

(1) $216   (2) 1200   (3) $90   (4) 2000

(5) Eng: 84, Maths: 81   (6) $81\dfrac{3}{5}$ kg

(7) 8500 kg   (8) $18,200

Exercise 12

A   (1) 72 mi/h   (2) 195 mi   (3) 6 h

B   (1) 82 km   (2) 850 km/h   (3) 9.75 km
     (4) 1:45 p.m.   (5) 153 mi   (6) 60 km
     (7) (a) Car A   (b) 7 km/h   (8) $68\dfrac{1}{5}$ km/h
     (9) 3 h   (10) $7\dfrac{1}{2}$ h

Exercise 13

(1) 40 mi/h   (2) 45 km   (3) 126 km

(4) 20 min   (5) 1:30 p.m.   (6) $13\dfrac{5}{7}$ km/h

Exercise 14

(1) 80 m/min (2) $3\frac{3}{8}$ h (3) $2\frac{1}{4}$ h
(4) 3187 m (5) 30 min (6) 60 km/h

Review 1

A (1) 3 (2) 3 (3) 4 (4) 4
(5) 2 (6) 2 (7) 2 (8) 1
(9) 3 (10) 1

B (1) $6\frac{1}{2}$ (2) $x - 10y$ (3) $\frac{9}{7}$ (4) 7:10
(5) 55 (6) 28.75 (7) 3.5 (8) 15
(9) 2500

C (1) $67\frac{1}{2}$ km/h
(2) Raoul: $480, Lisa: $160

Exercise 15

A (1) 9 (2) 10 (3) 28 (4) 20
(5) $22\frac{1}{2}$ (6) 12 (7) $4\frac{2}{7}$ (8) 15
(9) $\frac{4}{15}$ (10) $\frac{1}{9}$ (11) $\frac{1}{8}$ (12) $\frac{11}{15}$
(13) $\frac{1}{24}$ (14) $\frac{3}{16}$

B (1) $\frac{7}{12}$ (2) $\frac{14}{15}$ (3) $4\frac{4}{9}$ (4) $\frac{1}{3}$
(5) $\frac{3}{5}$ (6) $\frac{4}{5}$ (7) $1\frac{1}{2}$ (8) $\frac{1}{2}$
(9) $1\frac{1}{5}$ (10) $\frac{9}{20}$ (11) $\frac{16}{45}$ (12) 4
(13) 6 (14) $\frac{24}{25}$ (15) $2\frac{5}{8}$ (16) $5\frac{4}{9}$

Exercise 16

(1) 20 (2) 48 (3) 12 (4) 32

Exercise 17

A (1) $\frac{4}{15}$ (2) $3\frac{5}{6}$ (3) $\frac{1}{8}$ (4) $\frac{11}{12}$
(5) $\frac{3}{8}$ (6) $1\frac{1}{8}$ (7) 5 (8) $\frac{2}{3}$
(9) $\frac{1}{4}$ (10) 1 (11) $\frac{3}{8}$ (12) 6
(13) $1\frac{11}{25}$ (14) 2

B (1) $\frac{11}{15}$ (2) $\frac{1}{15}$ (3) $\frac{11}{16}$ (4) $\frac{1}{2}$
(5) $2\frac{3}{8}$ (6) $\frac{2}{45}$ (7) $\frac{2}{3}$ (8) $3\frac{2}{9}$

C (1) $\frac{1}{4}$ (2) $\frac{3}{5}$ (3) $\frac{1}{4}$ (4) $1\frac{1}{2}$
(5) 4 (6) 1 (7) $\frac{1}{6}$ (8) $\frac{1}{12}$

Exercise 18

(1) 42 (2) $516 (3) 31 (4) 3.2 lb
(5) $28\frac{1}{12}$ qt (6) 56 (7) 200
(8) 9 kg (9) $2500 (10) $\frac{1}{11}$

Exercise 19

A (1) 18.84 cm (2) 31.4 in. (3) 66 cm
(4) 22 ft

B (1) $2\frac{13}{32}$ m² (2) 28.26 cm² (3) 1.54 m²
(4) 78.5 cm²

Exercise 20

(1) $28\frac{4}{7}$ in (2) 9.42 cm² (3) $10\frac{5}{14}$ in.²
(4) 2.3 cm² (5) 3.44 cm² (6) 26.28 cm
(7) 12.56 m² (8) $1\frac{5}{7}$ cm² (9) 22.28 cm²
(10) 41.12 m (11) $16\frac{4}{7}$ cm (12) 58.875 cm²

Exercise 21

A (1) $\frac{1}{3}$ (2) 25 (3) 2 h (4) 4 : 1
(5) $66\frac{2}{3}$

B (1) 20 (2) 10 (3) $\frac{2}{5}$ (4) 66.7%
(5) 4 : 1 : 2

Exercise 22

A (1) $\frac{1}{5}$ (2) 12 (3) fairy tales
(4) 10 (5) 1 : 10

B (1) $\frac{1}{2}$ (2) 25 (3) 10
(4) 10 (5) 5 : 1

Exercise 23

A (1) 5 (2) $15 (3) $\frac{1}{2}$
(4) $5 (5) 3 : 5

B (1) 40 (2) $\frac{3}{10}$ (3) 520
(4) 40 (5) 8 : 6 : 5

Exercise 24

A (1) 56 cm³ (2) 96 cm³
(3) 168 cm³ (4) 144 cm³
B (1) 24 (2) 20
C (1) 6 cm (2) 12 cm

Exercise 25

(1) 9 in.　　(2) 25 cm²　　(3) 4 ℓ
(4) 24 cm　　(5) 14.4 ℓ　　(6) 150

Exercise 26

(1) 12.5 cm　　　(2) 5 ℓ
(3) 42　　　　　(4) 9 cm

Exercise 27

(1) 12.2 cm　　　(2) 6
(3) 2 cm　　　　(4) 4

Exercise 28

A (1) 30°　(2) 50°　(3) 60°　(4) 35°
B (1) 125°　(2) 70°　(3) 35°　(4) 110°
　(5) 60°　(6) 45°　(7) 20°　(8) 30°
C (1) 120°　(2) 80°　(3) 75°　(4) 90°
　(5) 104°　(6) 27°　(7) 85°　(8) 120°

Exercise 29

(1) 115°　　(2) 115°　　(3) 55°
(4) 80°　　(5) 35°　　(6) 152°
(7) 60°　　(8) 36°　　(9) 90°

Review 2

A (1) 2　　(2) 3　　(3) 1　　(4) 3
　(5) 4　　(6) 4　　(7) 2　　(8) 4
　(9) 2　　(10) 4　　(11) 2　　(12) 1
　(13) 1　　(14) 2　　(15) 4　　(16) 2
　(17) 4　　(18) 1　　(19) 2　　(20) 2

B (1) 4.6　　(2) 75　　(3) 60　　(4) $\frac{7}{3}$

　(5) $\frac{11}{14}$　　(6) 80　　(7) 10　　(8) $14\frac{2}{7}$

　(9) 5　　(10) 12.56　　(11) 2.80　　(12) 20

　(13) $\frac{1}{5}$　　(14) 3　　(15) 60　　(16) 72 lb

　(17) 12　　(18) $\frac{5}{24}$

C (1) 5 h　　　(2) $14,400　　(3) $1\frac{13}{15}$ m
　(4) 32.968 m

Review 3

A (1) 3　　(2) 1　　(3) 2　　(4) 4
　(5) 3　　(6) 4　　(7) 2　　(8) 3
　(9) 1　　(10) 1　　(11) 2　　(12) 1
　(13) 4
B (1) 70　　　(2) 135　　　(3) 20

　(4) 0.95　　(5) $36\frac{5}{6}$　　(6) $4m + 5$

　(7) 136　　(8) 50　　(9) 56

　(10) 2 : f　　(11) $\frac{d}{ab}$　　(12) 4

C (1) 416 cm³　　　　　(2) 1000 cm³

　(3) $\frac{1}{6}$ cup more　　　(4) 6 ft 2 in.

General Review 1

A (1) 4　　(2) 2　　(3) 2　　(4) 3
　(5) 1　　(6) 2　　(7) 4　　(8) 3
　(9) 1　　(10) 2　　(11) 4　　(12) 1
　(13) 3　　(14) 4　　(15) 2　　(16) 4
　(17) 3　　(18) 4　　(19) 3　　(20) 1

B (1) $12\frac{1}{2}$　(2) $\frac{3}{100}$　(3) 165　(4) 1105

　(5) 500　(6) 1004　(7) 100　(8) $\frac{3}{5}$

　(9) $\frac{36}{49}$　(10) $\frac{1}{2}$　(11) 628　(12) 45

C

D (1) $7.50　　(2) 4500 kg　　(3) 2.3 m

　(4) 36 kg　　(5) $4\frac{1}{6}$ h

General Review 2

A (1) 3　　(2) 2　　(3) 1　　(4) 4
　(5) 2　　(6) 3　　(7) 4　　(8) 3
　(9) 3　　(10) 1　　(11) 1　　(12) 3
　(13) 1　　(14) 2　　(15) 4　　(16) 4
　(17) 2　　(18) 2　　(19) 2　　(20) 3

B (1) $\frac{2}{25}$　　(2) 20　　(3) 1 : 3 : 5

　(4) 150　　(5) 5 : 7　　(6) 85
　(7) 22　　(8) 36　　(9) 80

　(10) 40　　(11) 3　　(12) $\frac{4}{15}$

C

D (1) $10　　(2) 7 oz　　(3) 36 ft²
　(4) 62　　(5) 7 cm

General Review 3

A (1) 1　　(2) 4　　(3) 1　　(4) 3
　(5) 1　　(6) 1　　(7) 2　　(8) 3
　(9) 4　　(10) 2　　(11) 4　　(12) 3
　(13) 4　　(14) 1　　(15) 3　　(16) 1
　(17) 2　　(18) 4　　(19) 4　　(20) 1

B (1) 1010   (2) 5   (3) 3
   (4) 100   (5) 2 m   (6) 39
   (7) 60   (8) 1.5   (9) 7.595
   (10) 50   (11) 60   (12) 880

C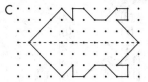

D (1) $30   (2) 44
   (3) (a) A : 30 (b) B : 18
   (4) 2 ℓ   (5) $259.05